Genetic Insights in
Paediatric Endocrinology
and Metabolism

BioScientifica LTD

16 The Courtyard, Woodlands
Bradley Stoke, Bristol BS32 4NQ, UK

© 1999 BioScientifica Ltd

British Library Cataloguing in Publication Data
A CIP catalogue record for this book is available from the British Library.

ISBN 1 901 978 06 0

Disclaimer
The papers contained in this book have been prepared and written by a medical writer based on oral presentations by the named authors. Accordingly, neither BioScientifica Ltd, Serono UK nor their officers, employees or agents are responsible for the accuracy or otherwise of any papers and shall have no liability for any claims, damages or losses however arising from the contents of any papers or use to which they may be put by any person.

Prepress by Fox Editorial and MPG Design
Cover design by John Stephens
Colour picture: Mehau Kulyk/Science Photo Library
Printed in Great Britain by Cambrian Printers Ltd, Aberystwyth

Foreword

In December 1998, Serono Pharmaceuticals Ltd held their 5th Cambridge Symposium at St John's College. The scientific organising committee for the meeting included Professor Albert Aynsley-Green, Dr Peter Clayton, Professor Dian Donnai, Dr David Dunger, Professor Ieuan Hughes, Professor James Leonard and Professor Steve O'Rahilly. They managed to gather together an outstanding international group of speakers to tackle the exciting interface between advances in molecular biology and clinical practice.

Cosseted in the halls and residences of the college, the speakers, audience and organisers were treated to the highest quality of clinical science and debate. The proceedings of the meeting are condensed in this small volume, and we hope they capture some of the excitement and enthusiasm that we experienced.

We are indebted to Serono Pharmaceuticals Ltd for their support and encouragement throughout the meeting and in bringing this volume to publication.

David B Dunger
Steve O'Rahilly

Contents

Leptin

Summary

Hyperinsulinaemia

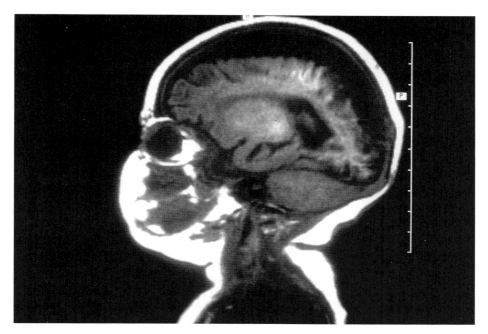

Figure 2 MRI brain scan in a 3-month old girl showing cerebral atrophy due to severe recurrent hypoglycaemia due to hyperinsulinism since birth.

Even if the condition is detected promptly and managed effectively so that neurological damage is avoided, the sequelae may be of great importance for the family since total pancreatectomy may be needed to control the hyperinsulinism, leading to the long-term consequences of diabetes.

Hypoglycaemia in childhood believed to be caused by hyperinsulinism was first described by Dannenberg *et al.* (1935) over 60 years ago. Since then it has been termed nesidioblastosis – the term nesidioblastoma being described in 1938 in adult pancreata (Laidlaw 1938) – persistent neonatal hyperinsulinaemic hypoglycaemia, islet cell dysregulation syndrome and persistent hyperinsulinaemic hypoglycaemia of infancy (PHHI). The term PHHI is gaining currency, even though it fails to encompass infants with transient hyperinsulinaemic hypoglycaemia.

Clinical presentation of hyperinsulinism

Hyperinsulinism presents in infancy, in childhood, and factitiously. An analysis of over 160 children treated in London (Great Ormond Street Hospital), Oxford, and Newcastle-upon-Tyne shows that the condition

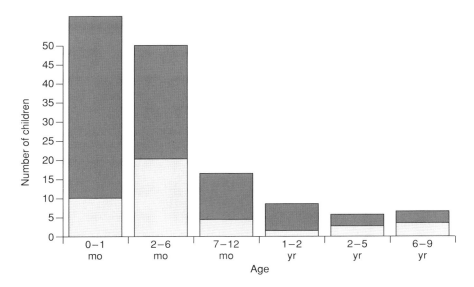

Figure 3 Age at presentation of children with hyperinsulinism (■), and proportions referred for surgery (□).

primarily affects children at birth and in early infancy, with relatively few patients appearing in later childhood. In many of these infants, the condition was transient or responded to medical treatment, and only one-quarter of the children needed surgery (Fig. 3).

Occasionally, factitious hyperinsulinism is seen in an otherwise normal child and is caused by the deliberate administration of insulin or a suphonylurea (e.g. glibenclamide). The clinician should maintain a high index of suspicion when atypical features in presentation occur; for example, severe hyperinsulinism arising in an older child.

Current clinical controversies in hyperinsulinism in childhood

These concern:
- whether transient, diazoxide-sensitive and resistant PHHI, and isolated adenoma in childhood are all the same disease;
- which are the important markers of pathophysiology at presentation;
- how to image and identify pancreatic 'hot-spots' of insulin release;
- whether medical or surgical management is best;
- which approach offers the best long-term outcome.

Diagnosis of hyperinsulinism

The newborn infant with hyperinsulinism typically has a high birthweight and resembles the child of a diabetic mother (implying the existence of prenatal hyperinsulinism). Not all infants have macrosomia, however, and affected premature or small-for-dates babies pose some of the most difficult diagnostic and management challenges.

The fact that hyperinsulinism can usually be diagnosed from one simple blood sample underlines the tragedy of delay, as in the example above. A sample *taken during a hypoglycaemic episode* reveals an inappropriate concentration of insulin (indeed the finding of any circulating insulin during hypoglycaemia is strongly suggestive) together with low blood levels of ketone bodies and fatty acids caused by the anabolic effects of insulin preventing lipolysis and ketogenesis.

Findings supporting the diagnosis include: high levels of C-peptide and proinsulin relative to matched controls; a glucose infusion rate >4–6 mg/kg per min needed to maintain blood glucose above 2.6–3.0 mmol/l; and a pronounced glycaemic responses to glucagon and/or somatostatin administration (Aynsley-Green *et al.*1981).

Diagnostic imaging

Among imaging modalities available are ultrasound (including direct intra-operative ultrasonography), computed tomography (CT), MRI, coeliac angiography, selective intra-arterial calcium stimulation (Albernethy *et al.* 1998), and percutaneous transhepatic pancreatic vein cannulation. In the last technique, developed by colleagues in Paris (Dubois *et al.* 1995), the pancreas is sequentially sampled as the cannula is withdrawn along the vein, while the patient is maintained under general anaesthesia in a hypoglycaemic state. The rather less difficult technique of selective stimulation of parts of the pancreas by calcium injected via the pancreatic arteries requires further validation.

During 63 attempts to image the pancreas in children in our series, we have detected only one insulinoma, by coeliac angiogram, in a 9-year-old girl with severe hypoglycaemia of recent onset. Pancreatic imaging rarely identifies focal areas in the neonate because of the small size of the organ. However, the ability to identify focal forms by such techniques is important, not only because curative resection of foci may be possible – as the impressive French outcome series shows (De Lonlay-Debeney *et al.* 1999) – but also for accurate location of focal forms. Much further work is needed to improve the ability to localise focal forms of hyperinsulinism.

Principles of management in PHHI

Management of PHHI that is more than empirical depends on an understanding of the pathophysiology of the condition. Until recently, it was believed to be purely an 'anatomical' disease, with insulin-secreting cells failing to aggregate to form normal islets of Langerhans. Insulin-secreting cells were noted to be present in duct epithelium and dispersed throughout the pancreas. It was these features that led to the term nesidioblastosis. However, these features may not be pathological and are not unique to hyperinsulinism. Thus, children dying from causes not associated with hypoglycaemia may have pancreata with these appearances and, conversely, children with normal-looking islets may still have severe hyperinsulinism.

The first steps leading to our understanding of the pathophysiology of PHHI came from our first series of children with 'nesidioblastosis'. Insulin secretion by islet cells *in vitro* was detected in the absence of glucose in the incubation medium with near-maximal insulin release in the presence of physiological concentrations of glucose (4 mmol/l). This was the first evidence of a dysregulation in the coupling of the concentration of glucose with the secretion of insulin (Aynsley-Green *et al.* 1981).

The next key development was the work by Glaser *et al.* (1990, 1994) on hyperinsulinism among 15 families of Ashkenazi Jews, Arabs and others in Israel, that implicated a mutation on the short arm of chromosome 11. This chromosome carries genes for two key proteins – a sulphonylurea receptor (SUR1) and the inward rectifier potassium channel Kir6.2 – that form a functional complex allowing the transport of potassium ions out of the β-cell. The genes for SUR and Kir6.2 are only 4.5 kilobase pairs apart. Two separate single-base mutations (guanine to adenine) of the SUR gene affecting K^+ transmembrane transport were then shown to be associated with familial PHHI (Thomas *et al.* 1995). Many other mutations have since been described, affecting both Kir6.2 itself and the first and second binding folds of SUR (Glaser *et al.* in press, Dunne *et al.* 1997*b*). Even more intriguing is the more recent report that patients with focal disease had a specific loss of heterozygosity on chromosome 11, with disappearance of the maternal allele and paternal imprinting (De Lonlay *et al.* 1997). Thus many different genotypes are being associated with PHHI (Glaser *et al.* in press)

Finally, as discussed in the next part of this chapter, new diseases have been described which lead to abnormalities in the ADP:ATP ratio in the cell that triggers insulin secretion without a primary defect in membrane ion transport.

Thus, it is now quite clear that the insulin secretion in PHHI is the final common endpoint arising from a number of underlying genetic, intracellular biochemical and membrane physiological disturbances. The clinical difficulty arises from the fact that there are at present few non-invasive means of determining which underlying process is afflicting any particular child.

II: Cellular and molecular aspects of unregulated insulin release

This part of the chapter discusses ways in which genomic features may be linked with membrane physiology and the clinical phenotype of PHHI. It presents a brief account of recent advances in the understanding of the molecular physiology of unregulated insulin secretion in PHHI. The study of isolated insulin-secreting cells from patients with PHHI has provided many insights into the cellular basis of this disease and shows how an integrated multidisciplinary approach involving scientists and clinicians can be beneficial to patients, and can enhance our understanding of normal physiological events.

Patch-clamp techniques

Insulin-secreting β-cells isolated from patients undergoing pancreatectomy for intractable hypoglycaemia have been studied using patch-clamp techniques in our laboratory. These high-resolution techniques have permitted the study of ionic currents, which regulate cellular processes, down to the level of single ion channels. With these procedures, we record currents measuring as little as 10^{-12}A. Various recording configurations have been utilised in the studies described here (Fig. 4). In all cases, the tip of a glass micropipette (diameter < 1 μm), containing a recording electrode, is tightly sealed onto the membrane of an intact cell. The resulting configuration is the 'cell-attached patch' and from this the activity of single ion channels situated in the portion of membrane trapped within the pipette tip can be recorded. If the micropipette is physically pulled away from the cell, the piece of membrane within the tip is ripped away resulting in an 'inside-out patch' which allows direct access to the cytoplasmic face of the ion channels. Alternatively, rupture of the membrane within the micropipette while in cell-attached mode produces the 'whole-cell' recording configuration, from which macroscopic currents representing the sum of activities of many ion channels across the entire membrane can be

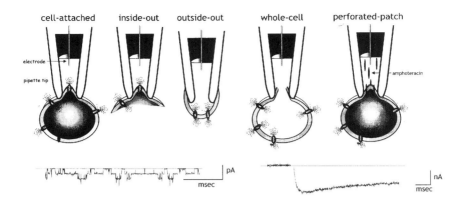

Figure 4 Schematic representation of the patch-clamp technique. Once tight contact has been established between a glass micropipette (with a tip diameter of <1 μm) and the cell membrane, individual ion channel events or whole cell macroscopic ion current recordings can be made. Using the cell-attached patch, inside-out and outside-out patch recording configurations, single ion channel events can be resolved, while the whole-cell and perforated patch configurations are used to record macroscopic currents. Typical 'single-channel current data' and 'whole cell' data are illustrated; note the differences in resolution of electrophysiological recordings using the different techniques. Inward currents are denoted by downward deflections from the zero current level represented by the line.

recorded. In addition, a subtle, but exquisite modification of the whole-cell configuration allows one to assess of the process of exocytosis in real time. This is dependent upon insulin secretory granules fusing with the cell membrane and increasing the cell 'capacitance', thus providing an accurate assessment of 'insulin secretion' from individual cells.

Ionic control of insulin release

The widely accepted consensus model of stimulus–secretion coupling which links glucose uptake and metabolism to insulin secretion is shown in Fig. 1 (also Dunne *et al.* 1997*a*). Our studies provide further evidence to substantiate this model and give important information on events that occur when the regulation of key components of the mechanism are disrupted.

Depolarisation-response coupling

At sub-stimulatory concentrations of glucose (< 3 mM), open ATP-sensitive K$^+$ (K$_{ATP}$) channels in the cell membrane allow the outward flux of K$^+$ ions thus maintaining the resting membrane potential close to the K^+ equilibrium potential of approximately $-70\,mV$.

Following glucose uptake and metabolism (Fig. 1, steps 1 & 2) the ATP/ADP ratio within the cell is increased and this causes K_{ATP} channel closure (step 3). The cell membrane potential then depolarises to $\approx -30\,mV$ (step 4) at which point voltage-dependent Ca^{2+} channels are activated (step 5). Finally, the resulting influx of Ca^{2+} ions into the cytoplasm triggers exocytosis of the insulin-containing secretory granules (step 6). The process of exocytosis is complex involving several complementary protein interactions (syntaxin, synaptotagmin, etc.) and this will not be reviewed here. An additional point of interest is that recent studies have identified sequences within the Ca^{2+} channels which may physically couple to secretory granules, and/or the protein(s) that govern exocytosis, thus demonstrating the proximal link between Ca^{2+} entry and insulin release (Wiser *et al.* 1999).

Clinical implications of the model

Since K_{ATP} channels play a pivotal role in stimulus–secretion coupling, agents that close these channels tend to mimic the action of glucose, while activators of these channels will have the opposite affect. Thus, the K_{ATP} channel opener, diazoxide, which provides a cornerstone of PHHI therapy, activates K_{ATP} channels, hyperpolarises the membrane potential, prevents voltage-dependent Ca^{2+} entry and thereby terminates insulin secretion. At the opposite end of the spectrum, sulphonylurea drugs, e.g. tolbutamide, cause closure of K_{ATP} channels, leading to membrane depolarisation, calcium entry and insulin secretion (Dunne *et al.* 1997*a*). This latter effect explains why sulphonylureas are so effective in the management of type 2 diabetes where there is insufficient insulin secretion for corresponding levels of glycaemia.

PHHI – a K_{ATP} channelopathy

The evidence

Since 1994 we have conducted research on isolated β-cells from 33 patients with PHHI, in collaboration with teams at Leicester University, Aberdeen University, Great Ormond Street Hospital and paediatric centres across the UK and Europe. In addition, β-cells isolated from more than 60 human cadaver donors have been studied in parallel control experiments and therefore serve as controls for the PHHI work. One of these donors was an age-matched control.

The first evidence that PHHI is a 'K_{ATP} channelopathy' came from observations of cell-attached patch recordings from β-cells isolated from PHHI patients. In cell-attached recordings of control β-cells, spontaneous K_{ATP} channel activity was seen and there was no spontaneous action potential activity at sub-stimulatory glucose concentrations. In marked contrast, similar recordings from PHHI β-cells were found to lack K_{ATP} channel openings and demonstrated spontaneous action potentials at sub-stimulatory glucose concentrations (Kane *et al*. 1996). These action potentials are generated by Ca^{2+} entry and this was demonstrated by the fact that they could be prevented by addition of the L-type Ca^{2+} channel blocker verapamil to the standard bathing solution. We recorded the cell membrane potential from PHHI β-cells and found this to be approximately –30 mV. This suggested that loss of K_{ATP} channel function rendered the cell incapable of controlling the resting membrane potential and thus resulting in spontaneous activation of voltage-dependent Ca^{2+} channels function (Dunne *et al*. 1997*a*). This particular observation was of immediate clinical relevance because it provided a rationale for the use of blockers of these channels, such as nifedipine in PHHI therapy. In this context we found that nifedipine significantly increased preprandial serum glucose and increased overnight fasting tolerance by 3-fold in a patient with persistent and severe hypoglycaemia despite a partial pancreatic resection (Lindley *et al*. 1996).

Additional evidence for loss of K_{ATP} channel function was provided by cell-free patch studies. Normally when an inside-out patch is formed there is a large increase in the magnitude of the spontaneous K_{ATP} current measured; this occurs because endogenous ATP levels within the β-cell usually inhibit around 95% of K_{ATP} channel activity. Thus after a patch is isolated, ATP levels drop and K_{ATP} channels open. In PHHI β-cells, however, the generation of inside-out patches does not cause K_{ATP} channel activity, providing further evidence that these channels are not functional in PHHI tissue.

The loss of K_{ATP} channel function alone is not sufficient to explain insulin hypersecretion. In Fig. 5 we have proposed that 'knock-out' of K_{ATP} channel function causes disruption of the resting membrane potential allowing the membrane to be permanently depolarised (step 1). We have confirmed that the resting membrane potential in PHHI β-cells is depolarised, and we believe that this in turn promotes constant unregulated Ca^{2+} influx (step 2) leading to elevated intracellular Ca^{2+} levels and inappropriate insulin hypersecretion (step 3) (Kane *et al*. 1996, Dunne *et al*. 1997*b*).

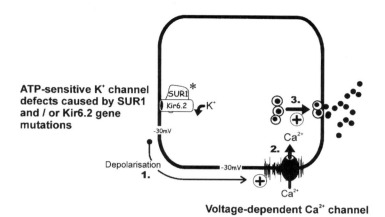

Figure 5 β-Cell K$_{ATP}$ channelopathy and unregulated insulin secretion. Persistent hyperinsulinaemic hypoglycaemia of infancy arises from defects (*) in either the KIR6.2 or SUR1 genes. Since these β-cells lack operational K$_{ATP}$ channels, the membrane potential remains depolarised (≈ −30 mV) in the absence of glucose metabolism (1). This leads to the persistent activation of voltage-dependent Ca^{2+} channels causing unregulated entry of Ca^{2+} (2) and persistent release of insulin as a consequence (3). Since functional K$_{ATP}$ channels are absent, patients with PHHI are unresponsive to medical therapy with the K$_{ATP}$ channel agonist diazoxide.

The K$_{ATP}$ channel

As mentioned in the chapter by Chaterjee, the functional K$_{ATP}$ channel in β-cells consists of a 'complex' of subunits, that comprises at least two different protein families. These are arranged in an obligatory octameric structure with the K$^+$-selective pore formed by four Kir6.2 protein subunits, surrounded by four larger SUR1 subunits. SUR1 is a member of the ATP-binding cassette family of proteins and acts as a conductance regulator for the pore (Fig. 6) (Aguilar-Bryan *et al.* 1998). Other disease-related ATP-binding cassette proteins include the cystic fibrosis transmembrane conductance regulator (CFTR) and the p-glycoprotein molecule which is associated with resistance to chemotherapy in long-term cancer patients.

ATP inhibits the K$_{ATP}$ channel complex through an interaction with Kir6.2, while ADP modulates the effects of ATP through its interaction with SUR1. Diazoxide and tolbutamide both operate on SUR1; much research is currently being directed at identifying the precise sites of action of these agents, as well as the parts of SUR1 and Kir6.2 that determine their 1:1 stoichiometry and trafficking to the membrane (Aguilar-Bryan *et al.* 1998, Ashcroft & Gribble 1998).

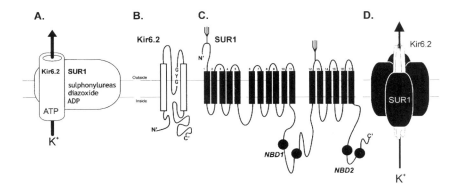

Figure 6 K_{ATP} channel architecture in pancreatic β-cells. (A) The key regulatory and pharmacological influences on K_{ATP} channels in pancreatic β-cells; ATP and K^+ conductance are controlled through the Kir6.2 subunit, while ADP, diazoxide and sulphonylurea (e.g. tolbutamide, glibenclamide)-induced channel gating are governed by SUR1. (B) The predicted topology of the K^+ channel subunit Kir6.2. (C) The predicted topology of the β-cell SUR1 gene product – an ATP-binding cassette protein. Note the characteristic high number of transmembrane spanning domains 1–17, two extracellular glycosylation sites and the presence of two intracellularly disposed nucleotide-binding domains (NBD) with Walker A and B binding motifs (●). (D) The heteromultimeric K_{ATP} channel complex is an obligatory octameric structure composed of (Kir6.2/SUR1)$_4$.

K_{ATP} channels are also found in other cells throughout the body but many of these channels have a slightly different subunit composition. For example, cardiac muscle K_{ATP} channels are composed of Kir6.2 and SUR2A, and smooth muscle K_{ATP} channels are formed by Kir6.2 and SUR2B.

Genetic defects and K_{ATP} channel function

Isolated β-cell studies have clearly documented that PHHI β-cells lack functional K_{ATP} channels (Kane *et al.* 1996, 1997, Dunne *et al.* 1997*b*) and this is supported by genetic information that mutations in the genes that encode SUR1 and Kir6.2 on Chromosome 11 are linked to 'familial' PHHI (Glaser *et al.* in press). One of our briefs is to study the effects of identified gene defects in Kir6.2 and SUR1 on β-cell function by engineering the gene defects and then expressing them in a recombinant system such as *Xenopus* oocytes or COS cells. This can provide vital structure–function information since gene defects can have diverse effects ranging from defective channel assembly or trafficking of subunits, to protein truncation and the total loss of K_{ATP} channels. From our ongoing studies we know that some identified mutations eradicate K_{ATP} channel activity, some significantly suppress it and yet others have little effect. This genetic heterogeneity is clearly of importance and is reflected in the clinical heterogeneity of patients presenting with symptoms of PHHI (see chapter by Hattersley).

The relevance of K_{ATP} channel defects to medical therapy for PHHI

Our data have documented how the loss of K_{ATP} channel function in the β-cell is associated with insulin hypersecretion. According to the model described in Fig. 5, these findings may also explain why some patients do not respond to medical therapy with diazoxide and somatostatin, since both of these agents normally operate by opening K_{ATP} channels. An added complexity in defining the cell dysfunction is that loss of K_{ATP} channels may also result in the up- or down-regulation of other types of ion channels. This may be advantageous in some instances since 'novel' ion channels may offer new protein targets for medical intervention and management of the disorder. We have recently described such a process in PHHI β-cells by characterising a small, diazoxide-sensitive 'K_{PHHI} channel' in patient tissue that lacked K_{ATP} channel function (Kane *et al.* 1997). This raises the possibility that treatment with high concentrations of diazoxide in the clinical environment might still be an effective way to terminate insulin release via this alternative channel. Indeed, we have been able to show that activation of K_{PHHI} channels leads to the inhibition of spontaneous electrical activity in PHHI β-cells (Kane *et al.* 1997).

Calcium entry and PHHI

Although many of our experimental results have implicated a role for unregulated calcium entry through voltage-dependent Ca^{2+} channels, in β-cells from some patients with PHHI we have been unable to record voltage-dependent Ca^{2+} entry. In these cases, unregulated Ca^{2+} influx may be explained by the up-regulation of alternative Ca^{2+} channels. One such candidate may be the I_{CRAN} (calcium release activated non-selective) channel, which usually opens when intracellular calcium stores are depleted. Therapeutic agents designed to affect the operation of these novel channels may be relevant in future for therapy of PHHI. In addition, we have also reported how the loss of regulated entry of Ca^{2+} in PHHI β-cells has aided *in vivo* diagnosis of focal forms of PHHI using the intra-arterial Ca^{2+}-stimulation test (Abernethy *et al.* 1998)

Current and future developments

The data discussed here show that PHHI may essentially be considered as a K_{ATP} channelopathy with an acquired dysregulation of calcium handling by the β-cell. The PHHI story is not yet complete since many questions about the disease remain unanswered, not least of which is the correlation of genotype–phenotype with the biology of β-cells in diseased tissue. We are, however, aided in these studies by recent findings that β-cells isolated from some PHHI patients will proliferate in culture; this provides a unique opportunity to study the disease on a day-to-day basis (Macfarlane *et al.* unpublished observations). We have also shown that transfection of these cells with the genes encoding Kir6.2, SUR1 and PDX-1 (an insulin gene transcription factor), can alleviate spontaneous insulin hypersecretion ('PHHI') *in vitro*. These experiments provide a rational basis to suggest the possibility that surgery coupled with *in vitro* cell engineering followed by auto-transplantation could be used as a novel therapy for PHHI. Finally, since the transgenic cell line continues to proliferate in culture, the possibility of developing human insulin-secreting glucose-responsive cell lines for transplantation-based therapy in diabetes also remains to be investigated.

III – Rational management of PHHI

This part of the chapter presents the summary and conclusions.

Intracellular pathophysiology of PHHI

The intracellular abnormalities associated with PHHI are summarised in Table 1.

Table 1 Intracellular abnormalities of PHHI

Defects in ATP generation involving glucokinase, glutamate dehydrogenase, and perhaps pyruvate dehydrogenase and other enzymes
Abnormal SUR/Kir6.2 structure and function
Upregulation of novel diazoxide-sensitive K^+ channels
Absence of voltage-regulated Ca^{2+} channels
Abnormal Ca^{2+}-regulated insulin exocytosis
Abnormal insulin gene transcription

Implications of cellular findings for clinical practice

The major current problem hindering the application of these cellular findings to clinical practice is the difficulty of assessing the nature of the underlying pathology. Only by obtaining the pancreas at surgery is it possible *in vitro* to define the locus of those conditions that cause abnormal ion transport. Elevated blood ammonia levels (Stanley *et al.* 1998), the identification of focal disease and the possibility of genotype screening may all be important, however.

Although the clinician is still working largely in the dark in being able quickly to identify pathophysiology when a new patient presents with hyperinsulinaemia, the aims of management are clear: to normalise glycaemia, frequency and content of feeding, fasting tolerance and 'orality' (the last term means the experience of feeding and of 'what the mouth is for' that allows normal psychosocial development and the preservation of family integrity).

Protecting the brain of the child with PHHI is the paramount goal, and the means of achieving this include:
• recognising hypoglycaemia early
• making a prompt diagnosis
• controlling immediate hypoglycaemia effectively
• managing hyperinsulinism adequately
• ensuring good compliance with treatment.

Despite these imperatives, it is disappointing that the occurrence of severe neurological handicaps is still so high. Thus, a recent German case analysis found that 20% of patents with PHHI are still profoundly handicapped – a proportion unchanged for 20 years. Ineffective immediate control of hypoglycaemia and poor long-term compliance with treatment are two of the key reasons for the poor outcome.

Current therapeutic strategies in PHHI

Hepatic glycogen laid down under the influence of insulin may be mobilised with glucagon, although this agent may not be effective alone for long-term therapy because it also stimulates insulin release. Potassium-channel openers (e.g. diazoxide + thiazide) and somatostatin may also be effective (although somatostatin also inhibits glucagon, which may need to be given concurrently), as may calcium-channel blocking agents. In addition, possibilities to restore intracellular ATP generation include a leucine-free diet in children with hyperammonaemia, and dichloroacetate (which could help correct a defect in children with hyperlactataemia due to pyruvate dehydrogenase inactivity (Aynsley-Green 1983).

The key management dilemma is whether patients resistant to diazoxide yet responsive to somatostatin should be subjected to a partial pancreatectomy – which if unsuccessful might lead to a total pancreatectomy – or receive combined continuous subcutaneous infusions of glucagon together with somatostatin (Landau & Glaser 1998).

A possible sequence of management options for PHHI is outlined in Table 2.

Corticosteroids, formerly proposed as treatment for PHHI, are, in our judgement, not to be recommended, because they are ineffective and increase the risks associated with subsequent surgery.

Psychosocial management is most important in families with infants who have PHHI, since the incidence of family break-ups is high. Affected children are often highly manipulative because of family preoccupation with preventing hypoglycaemia, they may suffer neurological handicap ranging from the subtle to the severe and they may indulge in self-destructive behaviours as adolescents which can include non-compliance with treatment.

Re-education to restore 'orality' is a very important aspect of the practical management of children with PHHI, the difficulty of which may be compounded by foregut dysmotility in which the normal pattern of the migrating complex in the proximal bowel is disrupted (Lindley *et al.* 1997).

PHHI – a systemic disease?

Several pieces of evidence suggest that PHHI should be considered a systemic disease. These include: the presence of hyperinsulinism together with hyperammonaemia; the coexistence of other hepatic metabolic disorders; and the possibility that abnormal SUR/Kir expression could be

Table 2 A proposed management cascade for PHHI

Glucose (most important in early stages)
Low leucine diet if ammonia levels are elevated
Diazoxide + thiazide
Nifedipine
Somatostatin + glucagon
Consider focal disease
Partial pancreatectomy ± medical treatment
Total pancreatectomy

associated with foregut dysmotility, pituitary dysfunction, cardiomegaly and neural dysfunction.

Conclusions – and the future

- The findings on the molecular biology and membrane physiology of the human pancreatic β-cell in health and in PHHI reported here provide a framework for understanding both normal and abnormal insulin secretion. They also give insights into the responsiveness of patients to medical therapy and open up new possibilities for novel drug therapies. PHHI-derived β-cells can now proliferate in culture, and have been used to show that *in-vitro* gene therapy can alleviate β-cell dysfunction.
- Although hyperinsulinism in infancy and childhood is a devastating disorder, the diagnostic cascade is now becoming more clearly defined.

For the future:

- Better diagnostic markers for the various β-cell dysfunctions are still needed.
- It is not yet known whether the pathophysiologies caused by different genetic abnormalities lead to different outcomes.
- Medical treatments need to be tailored to pathophysiology, with the focus on new drugs acting on intracellular energy metabolism and ionic transport processes.
- Histopathological and microsurgical techniques need to be refined.
- The development of molecular engineering and transplantation is potentially most important.

Acknowledgements

Research projects in our laboratories were supported by grants from the Medical Research Council and the British Diabetic Association. Clinical and scientific interactions in Europe are facilitated by a European Union-funded 'rare disease' initiative: Timo Otonkoski (Finland); Jacques Rahier (Belgium); Carina Ämmälä (Sweden); Jean-Marie Saudubray, Claudine Junien (France); Keith Lindley, Al Aynsley-Green, Roger James, Mark Dunne (UK); Ben Glaser (Israel); Wolfgang Rabl (Germany).

References

Abernethy LJ, Davidson CD, Lamont GL, Shepherd RM & Dunne MJ 1998 Intra-arterial calcium stimulation in the investigation of hyperinsulinaemic hypoglycaemia. *Archives of Disease in Childhood* 78 359–363.

Aguilar-Bryan L, Clement IV JP, Gonzalez G, Kunjilwar K, Babenko A & Bryan J 1998 Toward understanding the assembly and structure of K_{ATP} channels. *Physiological Reviews* **78** 227–245.

Ashcroft FM & Gribble FM 1998 Correlating structure and function in ATP-sensitive K^+ channels. *Trends in Neuroscience* **21** 288–294.

Aynsley-Green A, Polak JM, Bloom SR, Gough MH, Keeling J, Ashcroft SJH, Turner RC & Baum JD 1981 Nesidioblastosis of the pancreas: definition of the syndrome and the clinical management of severe neonatal hyperinsulinaemic hypoglycaemia. *Archives of Disease in Childhood* **56** 496–508.

Aynsley-Green A, Weindling AM, Soltész G & Jenkins PA 1983 Transient lactic acidosis and hyperalaninaemia associated with neonatal hyperinsulinaemic hypoglycaemia: the effects of dichloroacetate (DCA). *European Journal of Pediatrics* **141** 117–119.

Aynsley-Green A, Dunne MJ, James RFL & Lindley KJ 1998 Ions and genes in persistent hyperinsulinaemic hypoglycaemia of infancy; a commentary on the implications for tailoring treatment to disease pathogenesis. *Journal of Paediatric Endocrinology* **11** 121–129.

Beinbrech B, Wendel U & Mayatepek E 1999 Datenbank für Patienten mit kongenitalem Hyperinsulinismus – erste Ergebnisse. In *'Nesidioblastose' Von der Moleklaren Pathophysiologie zur Therapie*, pp 83–97. Eds W Rabl & K Mohnike. Heidelberg: Johann Ambrosius Barth.

Dannenberg AM, Bell MA & Gouley B 1935 Spontaneous hypoglycaemia due to hyperinsulinism in child; report of case with autopsy findings. *Journal of Paediatrics* **7** 44–54.

de Lonlay P, Fournet J-C, Rahier J, Gross-Morand MS, Poggi-Travert F, Fouasier V *et al.* A somatic deletion of the imprinted 11p15 region in sporadic persistent hyperinsulinaemic hypoglycaemia of infancy is specific of focal adenomatous hyperplasia and endorses partial pancreatectomy. *Journal of Clinical Investigation* **100** 802–807.

de Lonlay-Debeney P, Poggi-Travert F, Fournet J-C *et al.* 1999 Clinical features of 52 neonates with hyperinsulinism. *New England Journal of Medicine* **340** 1169–1175.

Dubois J, Brunelle F, Touati G *et al.* 1995 Hyperinsulinism in chidlren: diagnostic value of pancreatic venous sampling correlated with clinical, pathological and surgical outcome in 25 cases. *Pediatric Radiology* **25** 512-6.

Dunne MJ, Aynsley-Green A & Lindley KJ 1997*a* Nature's K_{ATP} channel knock out; PHHI a K^+ channel disorder of pancreatic b-cells leading to hypersecretion of insulin. *News in Physiological Sciences* **12** 197–203.

Dunne MJ, Kane C, Shepherd RM, Sanchez G, James RFL, Johnson PRV, Aynsley-Green A, Lu S, Clement JP, Lindley KJ, Seino S & Aguilar-Bryan L 1997*b* Familial persistent hyperinsulinemic hypoglycaemia of infancy and mutations in the sulfonylurea receptor. *New England Journal of Medicine* **336** 703–706.

Glaser B, Phillip M, Carmi R, Lieberman E & Landau H 1990 Persistent hyper-insulinemic hypoglycemia of infancy ('nesidioblastosis'): autosomal recessive inheritance in 7 pedigrees. *American Journal of Medical Genetics* **37** 511–515.

Glaser B, Chiu KC, Anker R *et al.* 1994 Familial hyperinsulinism maps to chromosome 11p14-15.1, 30 cM centromeric to the insulin gene. *Nature Genetics* **7** 185–188.

Glaser B, Kesavan P, Heyman M *et al.* 1998 Familial hyperinsulinism caused by an activating glucokinase mutation. *New England Journal of Medicine* **338** 226–230.

Glaser B, Thornton P, Otonkoski T & Junien C in press The genetics of neonatal hyperinsulinism. *Archives of Disease in Childhood.*

Kane C, Lindley KJ, Johnson PRV, James RFL, Milla PJ, Aynsley-Green A & Dunne MJ 1997 Therapy for persistent hyperinsulinaemic hypoglycaemia of infancy (PHHI); understanding the responsiveness of β-cells to diazoxide and somatostatin. *Journal of Clinical Investigation* **100** 1888–1893.

Kane C, Shepherd RM, Squires PE Johnson PRV, , James RFL, Milla PJ, Aynsley-Green A, Lindley KJ & Dunne MJ 1996 Loss of functional K$_{ATP}$ channels in β-cells causes persistent hyperinsulinaemic hypoglycaemia of infancy. *Nature Medicine* **2** 1344–1347.

Laidlaw GF (1938) Nesidioblastosis, the islet cell tumour of the pancreas. *American Journal of Pathology* **14** 125–134.

Landau H & Glaser B 1998 Conservative treatment and long-term follow-up of persistent hyperinsulinism of infancy (HI). *Second International Conference on ATP-Sensitive Potassium Channels and Disease*, pp 33–38. St Charles, USA: Giovanni Lorenzini Medical Foundation.

Lindley KJ, Dunne MJ, Kane C, Shepherd RM, Squires PE, James RFL, Johnson PRV, Eckhart S, Wakeling E, Dattani M, Milla PJ & Aynsley-Green A 1996 *In vitro* studies of the ionic control of β-cell function in nesidioblastosis. Does calcium channel blockade offer a new therapeutic opportunity? *Archives of Disease in Childhood* **74** 373–378.

Lindley KJ, Knafelz D, St Louis D, Dunne MJ, Aynsley-Green A & Milla PJ 1997 Surface electrogastrographic evidence of foregut dysmotility in persistent hyperinsulinaemic hypoglycaemia of infancy (PHHI). *Journal of Physiology* 499P:108P.

Stanley CA, Leu YK, Hsu BY *et al.* 1998 Hyperinsulinism and hyperammonemia in infants with regulatory mutations of the glutamate dehydrogenase gene. *New England Journal of Medicine* **338** 1352–1357.

Straub SG, James RFL, Dunne MJ & Sharp GWG 1998*a* Glucose activates both K$_{ATP}$ channel-dependent and K$_{ATP}$ channel-independent signaling pathways in human islets. *Diabetes* **47** 758–764.

Straub SG, James RFL, Dunne MJ & Sharp GWG 1998*b* Glucose augmentation of mastoparan-stimulated insulin secretion in rat and human pancreatic islets. *Diabetes* **47** 1053–1057.

Thomas PM, Cote GJ, Wohllk N *et al.* 1995 Mutations in the sulfonylurea receptor gene in Familial Hyperinsulinemic Hypoglycemia of Infancy. *Science* **268** 426–429.

Wiser O, Trus M, Hernandez A, Renstrom E, Barg S, Rorsman P & Atlas D 1999 The voltage-sensitive Lc-type Ca^{2+} channel is functionally coupled to the exocytotic machinery. *Proceedings of the National Academy of Sciences (USA)* **96** 248–253.

Genetic Insights in Paediatric Endocrinology and Metabolism
Eds S O'Rahilly and D B Dunger
BioScientifica Ltd, Bristol (1999)

The hyperinsulinaemia-hyperammonaemia syndrome: gain-of-function mutations of glutamate dehydrogenase

C A Stanley

Endocrine Division, Children's Hospital of Philadelphia, Philadelphia, PA, USA

Congenital hyperinsulinism is the commonest cause of hypoglycaemia in young infants. Both recessive and dominant forms of hyperinsulinism have been identified that affect the pathways regulating pancreatic β-cell function. We have recently discovered an unusual form of hyperinsulinism associated with persistently elevated levels of plasma ammonium – the hyperinsulinism-hyperammonaemia (HI/HA) syndrome – the genetic causes of which are gain-of-function mutations in the gene for the mitochondrial enzyme glutamate dehydrogenase (GHD) (Weinzimer *et al.* 1997, Stanley *et al.* 1998, Zammarchi *et al.* 1996). The HI/HA syndrome may be a relatively common form of hyperinsulinism, it is much milder and of later onset than hyperinsulinism caused by potassium channel defects, and it is readily diagnosed and treated.

Hyperinsulinism

Hyperinsulinism may be transient or congenital.

- **Transient hyperinsulinism** occurs in infants of diabetic mothers, and in the 'stress-induced' form which is poorly understood (Collins et al. 1990).
- **Congenital hyperinsulinism** may be due to: recessive mutations affecting the potassium channel (SUR1, Kir6.2) as described in the chapter by Aynsley-Green *et al.*; dominant defects affecting glucokinase (GK) (Glaser et al. 1998) and glutomate dehydrogenase (GDH); and non-Mendelian paternal transmission of potassium channel mutations (focal hyperinsulinism) (Verkarre *et al.* 1998, Ryan *et al.* 1998).

Figure 1 summarises the mechanisms in the β-cell whereby glucose stimulates insulin secretion, showing the sites affected by the potassium channel, GK and GDH mutations. The GK defect, which has been described from a single family, has the effect of maintaining insulin secretion until blood glucose level reaches abnormally low levels of about 1.5 mM (Glaser *et al.* 1998).

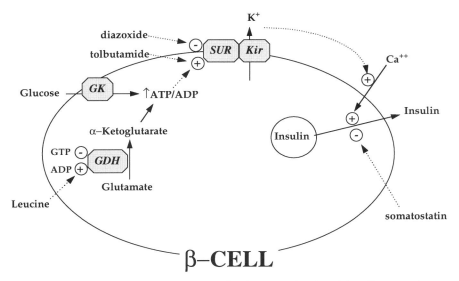

Figure 1 Diagram of the pancreatic β-cell, glucose-stimulated insulin secretion and sites affected by the potassium channel, glucokinase (GK) and glucose dehydrogenase (GDH) mutations.

The HI/HA syndrome

The GDH mutations responsible for the HI/HA syndrome affect the pathways by which amino-acids – particularly leucine – stimulate insulin secretion. Clinically, affected patients are not large-for-dates, and present late (at about one year) with mild hypoglycaemia which is highly sensitive to diazoxide. They also show a persistent four- to eightfold elevation in plasma ammonium levels compared to the normal values of 9–33 μmol/litre, but have no typical symptoms of hyperammonaemia.

Among our series of 25 patients with the HI/HA syndrome, the defect was sporadic in 20, but five showed a vertical transmission pattern consistent with dominant inheritance. In one family, the father of two affected daughters who presented at 11 months of age had originally been diagnosed with leucine-sensitive hypoglycaemia at the same age. Measurements of plasma ammonium in these three individuals leading to the definitive diagnosis of HI/HA syndrome were prompted by the discovery of the GDH defect in other families. The level in the unaffected mother is a high normal 30 μmol/l, while that of the father is 82 μmol/l, the daughters' levels are 88 and 100 μmol/l, and the father's own parents had normal levels (female 19, male 17 μmol/l). Evidently the father has a *de novo* GDH mutation.

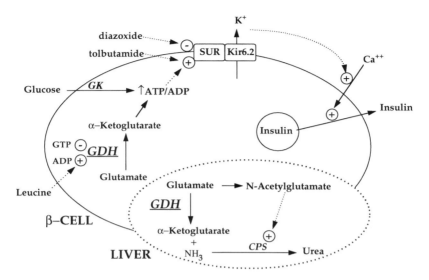

Figure 2 Diagram of the pancreatic β-cell, summarising the twin key roles of GDH suggesting that GDH gene defects might be responsible for HI/HA. Leucine stimulates insulin secretion by activating GDH; and from glutamate is produced *N*-acetylglutamate (NAG), which triggers allosteric activation of carbamyl phosphate synthetase (CPS) – the first step in the conversion of ammonia to urea. (Reproduced from Stanley *et al.* 1998 with permission.)

GDH and the HI/HA syndrome

GDH is encoded solely by the GLUD1 gene on chromosome 10. It was first selected as a candidate gene for the defect responsible for HI/HA for two main reasons (Fig. 2). First, leucine stimulates insulin secretion by acting as an allosteric activator of GDH, thus increasing glutamate oxidation to α-ketoglutarate in the Krebs cycle and initiating the ATP/ADP cascade described in the previous paper.

Secondly, the intracellular pool of glutamate is a key regulatory factor for ammonia metabolism; glutamate is the substrate for the production of *N*-acetylglutamate (NAG), which triggers allosteric activation of carbonyl phosphate synthetase (CPS) – the first step in the conversion of ammonia to urea.

Hypothesis for a GDH-mediated pathophysiology of HI/HA

Our hypothesis is that in the pancreatic β-cell excessive GDH activity due to a gain-of-function mutation leads to excessive oxidation of glutamate,

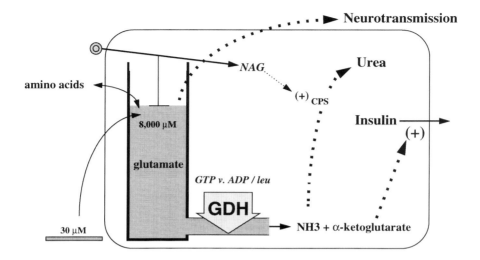

Figure 3 GDH controls metabolic signalling in the pancreatic β-cell. The high levels of glutamate act as a 'float valve' to regulate the formation of N-acetylglutamate (NAG) and so of urea. Increased intracellular ATP or leucine activates GDH, increasing glucose oxidation, stimulating insulin secretion, depleting the glutamate pool and increasing the levels of ammonia for urea synthesis.

increased ATP level and increased insulin release. At the same time, in the liver excessive GDH activity depletes the glutamate pool, decreases NAG formation, and so down-regulates ureagenesis. Thus the same GDH defect, operating in both the β-cell and the liver, causes both hypoglycaemia and ammonaemia, the two major manifestations of the HI/HA syndrome.

What feature of GDH could be involved in the increased activity? GDH forms a homohexamer and normally catalyses the reversible reaction:

$$\text{Glutamate} + \text{NAD} \longleftrightarrow \alpha\text{-ketoglutarate} + NH_4^+ + \text{NADH}$$

ADP and leucine are allosteric activators of GDH, whereas GTP, NADH, oestrogen and palmityl-CoA are allosteric inhibitors of enzyme activity (Colman 1991). It appears that the active site and allosteric binding site are at opposite ends of the enzyme, so that a mutation may be postulated that would modify allosteric regulation without affecting enzyme activity. Our hypothesis also had to assume: first, that in HI/HA the reaction catalysed by GDH would run irreversibly in the direction of glutamate oxidation so that increased GDH activity resulted in increased flow; and secondly, that the activity of the enzyme was normally switched off.

The intracellular glutamate pool as a 'float valve' for metabolic signalling

As a neurotransmitter, glutamate should not be abundant in plasma, and consequently the concentration of intracellular glutamate (Fig. 3) is enormous (8 mM) compared to that of the blood (<30 μM). The intracellular glutamate pool is replenished from amino-acid transamination. As Fig. 3 shows, the high levels of glutamate act as a 'float valve' to regulate the formation of NAG and hence also of urea. To maintain the intracellular pool the GDH reaction must be inactive. Activating GDH in the β-cell by increasing the concentration of ADP or leucine increases glucose oxidation, stimulates insulin secretion, depletes the glutamate pool, and simultaneously increases the levels of ammonia for urea synthesis.

In addition, GHD acts as a neurotransmitter in the brain, and its overactivity in HI/HA syndrome might prevent the brain from developing increased glutamate, and cause hyperammonaemic neurotoxicity. Hence hyperactivity of GDH in the brain may be important in the context of the clinical syndrome.

Testing the hypothesis for a GDH-mediated pathophysiology in HI/HA

This hypothesis was tested by observing GDH activity, and its regulation by GTP and ADP *in vitro*, in normal lymphoblasts and lymphoblasts from patients with HI/HA. Enzyme activity was increased by ADP and inhibited by GTP in normal cells, but the sensitivity to inhibition of enzyme activity by GTP was about fivefold less in patients' than in control cells, resulting in an increase in enzyme function. The diminished response to GTP inhibition was the only abnormality of enzyme control found in the HI/HA patients.

HI/HA mutations in GDP

The map of mutation sites in the cDNA of patients with the HI/HA syndrome is shown in Fig. 4. All the mutations so far found appear in exons 11 and 12, which is thought to be the domain conferring allosteric regulation of the enzyme, and all are closely mapped into a region of 14 amino-acids. Of the mutations from the 23 probands shown, the commonest, serine-to-leucine, has been found in nine.

The affected father and two daughters mentioned above have normal fasting tolerance but have a history of a highly sensitive hypoglycaemic response to protein feeding. For example, an oral protein load of 1 g/kg body weight caused the father's plasma glucose to drop from 3.5 mM to 2.0 mM within 2 hours, while his plasma insulin level rose and remained

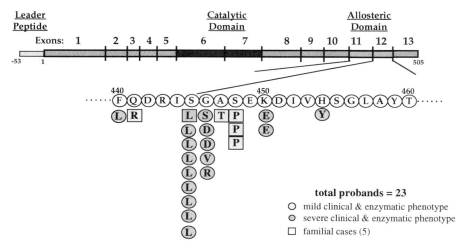

Figure 4 Map of mutation sites in the GDH cDNA of patients with the HI/HA syndrome. All known mutations appear in exons 11 and 12, the putative allosteric enzyme regulation domain.

inappropriately high, at 12 μIU/ml. An acute insulin reaction (up to 25 μIU/ml), together with a decline in plasma glucose, was also elicited by a intravenous bolus injection of leucine in the younger affected daughter.

This clinical picture resembles that of 'leucine-sensitive hypoglycaemia of infancy', which was described by Cochrane in 1955 (Cochrane *et al.* 1955). It was later shown that leucine could stimulate insulin secretion in isolated islets, even in normal individuals who had been primed by sulphonylurea treatment (Fajans *et al.* 1967). In the 1970s it was becoming clear that hypo-glycaemic infants also had hyperinsulinism (Stanley & Baker 1976) and we made the assumption that leucine sensitivity was always associated with congenital hyperinsulinism. However, the HI/HA syndrome is now better understood and it is likely that leucine/protein-sensitive hyperinsulinism is restricted to patients with GDH mutations. Furthermore, patients with SUR defects, as described in the chapter by Aynsley-Green *et al.*, probably do not suffer from leucine hypersensitivity.

In another large family (Kukuvitis *et al.* 1997) with dominantly transmitted hyperinsulinism caused by a GDH mutation, survival has ranged from a few months to over 70 years. Such heterogeneity of expression in the GDH defect probably depends on dietary changes, and this should be borne in mind in the clinical setting. Individuals diagnosed with hypoglycaemia in the third generation have been controlled quite well by treatment with diazoxide.

Table 1 Key regulatory roles of GDH

Site of action	System regulated
β-cell	Protein- and amino-acid-stimulated insulin secretion Maintenance of basal fasting insulin secretion
Liver	Protein oxidation/catabolism (e.g. ammonia detoxification)
Brain	Maintenance of the glutamate neurotransmitter pool
Kidney	Ammoniagenesis (and thereby renal acid excretion)

Newly-recognised regulatory roles for GDH

The central role of GDH in the HI/HA syndrome provokes consideration of major regulatory roles of this enzyme in other pathways. Table 1 summarises the known and suspected key roles of GDH in the pancreatic β-cell, liver, brain and kidney, which should continue to be investigated.

Conclusions

- Although newly described, the HI/HA syndrome due to a GDH defect may be relatively common, and could be the second most frequent cause of hyperinsulinism.
- Clinically, HI/HA is much milder than hyperinsulinism caused by potassium channel defects affecting SUR1 and Kir6.2, is diazoxide responsive and is of later onset.
- HI/HA is easily recognised from a casual blood ammonia determination showing elevation into the range of 80–200 μM.
- HI/HA can be familial with dominant transmission of mutations in the inhibitory domain of the GDH gene, or sporadic.
- In contrast to hyperinsulinism caused by potassium channel defects, HI/HA is eminently treatable; patients respond very well to diazoxide with or without protein restriction.
- Studying genetic defects such as the GDH mutations responsible for the HI/HA syndrome provides new information about normal physiology which have not emerged from basic biochemical studies.

References

Cochrane WA, Payne WW, Simpkiss MJ & Woolf LI 1955 Familial hypoglycaemia precipitated by aminoacids. *Journal of Clinical Investigation* **35** 411–422.

Collins JE, Leonard JV, Teale D, Marks V, Williams DM, Kennedy CR *et al.* 1990 Hyperinsulinaemic hypoglycemia in small for dates babies. *Archives of Disease of Childhood* **65** 1118–1120.

Colman RF 1991 Glutamate dehydrogenase (bovine liver). In: *A study of enzymes*, pp 173–192. Ed SA Kuby. New York: CRC Press,.

Fajans SS, Floyd FC, Knopf RF, Guntshe EM, Rull JA, Thiffault CA *et al.* 1967 A difference in the mechanism by which leucine and other amino acids induce insulin release. *Journal of Clinical Endocrinology and Metabolism* **27** 1600–1606.

Glaser B, Kesavan P, Heyman M, Davis E, Cuesta A, Buchs A *et al.* 1998 Familial hyperinsulinism caused by an activating glucokinase mutation. *New England Journal of Medicine* **338** 226–230.

Kukuvitis A, Deal C, Arbour L & Polychronakos C 1997 An autosomal dominant form of familial persistent hyperinsulinaemic hypoglycaemia of infancy, not linked to the sulfonylurea receptor locus. *Journal of Clinical Endocrinology and Metabolism* **82** 1192–1194.

Ryan F, Devaney D, Joyce C, Nestorowicz A, Permutt MA, Glaser B *et al.* 1998 Hyperinsulinism: molecular aetiology of focal disease. *Archives of Disease of Childhood* **79** 445–447.

Stanley CA & Baker L 1976 Hyperinsulinism in infants and children: diagnosis an therapy. *Advances in Pediatrics* **23** 315–355.

Stanley CA, Lieu YK, Hsu BYL, Burlina AB, Greenberg CR, Hopwood NJ *et al.* 1998 Hyperinsulinism and hyperammonaemia in infants with regulatory mutation of the glutamate dehydrogenase gene. *New England Journal of Medicine* **338** 1352–1357.

Verkarre V, Fournet JC, de Lonlay P, Gross-Morand MS, Devillers M, Rahier J *et al.* 1998 Paternal mutation of the sulphonylurea (SUR1) gene and maternal loss of 11p15 imprinted genes lead to persistent hyperinsulinism in focal adenomatous hyperplasia. *Journal of Clinical Investigation* **102** 1286–1291.

Weinzimer SA, Stanley CA, Berry GT, Yudkoff M, Tichman M & Thornton PS 1997 A syndrome of congenital hyperinsulinism and hyperammonaemia. *Journal of Pediatrics* **130** 661–664.

Zammarchi E Filippi L, Novembre E & Donati MA 1996 Biochemical evaluation of a patients with a familial form of leucine-sensitive hypoglycaemia and concomitant hyperammonaemia. *Metabolism* **45** 957–960.

Hypoglycaemia and the child's brain

E J Novotny Jr[1,2] D Rothman[3] and W Tamborlane[1]

Departments of Pediatrics[1], Neurology[2] and Diagnostic Imaging[3], Yale University, School of Medicine, 333 Cedar Street, PO Box 8064, New Haven, CT 06520-8064, USA

Because hypoglycaemic syndromes are most prevalent in the neonate and can have devastating consequences on the developing nervous system, it is important to understand cerebral metabolism in the maturing nervous system and the associated neuroanatomical and neurophysiological changes that occur with development.

There are still many unanswered questions about the impact of hypoglycaemia on the developing human nervous system. New direct, non-invasive nuclear magnetic resonance (NMR) spectroscopic techniques for studying brain glucose and energy metabolism are just beginning to provide insights into the mechanisms of brain injury and dysfunction associated with hypoglycaemia.

Normal brain development in the neonate

At birth, the brain is nearly identical to that of the adult with respect to gross neuroanatomy; it reaches adult size in the first decade of life. The number of neurons at birth is similar to adults, but glia continue to increase in number and size during the first decade of life. This occurs during the process of myelination and synaptogenesis.

This latter process is most active during the first few years of life and correlates with the development of energy metabolism, glial–neuronal interactions and neurotransmitter release. The processes of synapse formation and synaptic pruning are activity dependent.

Ultimately, the mature nervous system is dependent on a high rate of oxidative metabolism of glucose for neurotransmitter release, maintenance of ion gradients and normal function. A unique system of compartmentation of brain metabolism between glia and neurons develops over this time. During development, cell death occurs by both apoptosis and necrosis under a variety of conditions that are closely linked to metabolic processes.

Cerebral metabolism in the immature nervous system

Overall, the rate of energy metabolism is significantly less in the immature than in the mature brain. Glucose is the major substrate for the two major cell types in the brain, neurons and glia. However, the immature nervous system can more readily utilise alternative substrates, including lactate and ketone bodies. These substrates can be used by the mature nervous system to sustain normal function only under specialised circumstances.

During development there are significant changes in the distribution and number of the major glucose transporter (type 1) at the blood–brain barrier. A neuron-specific glucose transporter (type 3) also appears with maturation. In addition to this transporter, several other transporters (monocarboxylic acid transporters) and several enzyme systems increase and are redistributed in specific cell types and compartments (Vannucci et al. 1994).

Neurotransmission is the critical process for normal brain function and involves interactions among the many different cell types in the developing brain. Glutamate is the major excitatory neurotransmitter in the brain. The cell–cell interactions of this neurotransmitter and its relationship to metabolism are particularly important in brain injury. A process known as 'excitotoxic' cell injury involves this neurotransmitter and is observed in hypoglycaemic brain injury. Many other forms of brain injury arise from this process in both adults and children.

A great deal of information is known about the role of glia and glia–neuronal interactions involved with glutamate neurotransmission under normal and pathological conditions. The glutamate that is released from neurons is taken up into glia and converted to glutamine. Glutamine synthesis is compartmentalised in glia and is critical in the maintenance of low extracellular concentration of glutamate. The glutamine is then transported back to neurons where it is converted back to glutamate. This glutamate–glutamine cycle is highly dependent on the oxidative metabolism of glucose in the mature nervous system.

Alternative energy substrates

The potential of alternative substrates to sustain normal brain function or prevent brain injury in the developing nervous system has been the subject of several investigations. Many studies in mammalian species have shown that the immature nervous system has an increased capacity to use both lactate and ketone bodies. Recent studies have suggested that in the mature nervous system, glia convert glucose to lactate that is then used by neurons as the primary source for energy metabolism. In studies in rats, the brain metabolises glucose and other substrates at a relatively low metabolic rate during the first few days of life. At approximately 15 days of age in the rat, the brain switches to oxidative metabolism of glucose, which more efficiently generates ATP at the higher levels, required for neurotransmitter release and other processes (Nehlig *et al.* 1993). The glutamatergic neurotransmitter system reaches maturity at this time. The exact timing and distribution of these changes in the human brain during development are not known, but the changes in glucose metabolism in the human brain during development have been measured with positron emission tomography (PET) (Chugani *et al.* 1987, Kinnala *et al.* 1996). The changes in glucose metabolism measured by PET parallel the alterations observed in the development of specific functions. Glucose metabolism is barely detectable in the neonate's brain and is limited to the brainstem, thalamus and diencephalon. Metabolism increases throughout childhood as motor, cognitive and sensory function increase. Glucose metabolism during infancy is low compared with the adult. Whole brain metabolism in the latter portion of the first decade of life is approximately 20% greater than the adult and gradually decreases with age. This period of relatively high glucose metabolism may increase the vulnerability of the developing brain to hypoglycaemia and other insults that effect energy metabolism.

NMR spectroscopy of the human brain

My colleagues and I have recently developed several non-invasive methods using NMR spectroscopy (NMRS) to investigate brain glucose metabolism in the immature nervous system. NMR imaging has revolutionised our ability to examine the anatomy of the brain, but extensions of this technique now allow brain metabolism to be studied in humans *in vivo.* Using these methods a region of interest, in the occipital cortex comprised primarily of grey matter, is selected from a NMR image. After optimisation of the system to detect the desired constituents (e.g. glucose, amino-acids) the NMR signals are acquired over a few or several minutes.

Proton NMR – glucose metabolism

Proton NMR can detect signals from protons in glucose at the concentration normally found in the brain (i.e. 1.0 mM), but overlapping proton signals from other molecules do not permit direct measurement of glucose. However, we performed proton NMR studies on subjects during a 10- to 20-minute intravenous infusion designed to increase serum glucose from normoglycaemia (3–5 mM) to hyperglycaemia (10–15 mM). We subtracted the normoglycaemic from the hyperglycaemic spectra to give a clear series of glucose proton peaks corresponding with those proton NMR signals detected from a pure sample of glucose.

This knowledge about the proton NMR spectrum of the glucose in the human brain has made possible the non-invasive detection of changes in brain glucose transport properties and kinetics under different experimental conditions. Several baseline spectra are obtained during normoglycaemia and a steady-state hyperglycaemic phase is induced (e.g. at about 18 mM) by infusion of glucose during which further glucose proton NMR spectra are obtained. From the measured glucose changes in the serum and NMR measured changes in brain glucose concentration as a function of time, the kinetic parameters of brain glucose transport can be derived from a simplified Michaelis–Menten model. In a typical experiment, an assumption that during infusion the region of the brain studied had a constant rate of glucose metabolism is made and the K_T was calculated to be 4.8 ± 2.4 mM, and the T_{max} 0.8 ± 0.45 mmol/g/min (Gruetter *et al.* 1996).

In a young patient diagnosed with a rare glucose transport defect, this technique was able to detect a 50% defect in glucose transport. In addition to these proton NMR studies of glucose, proton NMR can measure steady-state concentrations of glutamate, glutamine, lactate, aspartate and other metabolites in the human brain (Novotny *et al.* 1998).

^{13}Carbon NMR – glucose and amino-acid metabolism

Proton NMRS can be used to measure steady-state levels of glucose and amino-acids in the brain, and also reveal the kinetics of glucose transport, but another method, ^{13}C NMR spectroscopy can provide more specific metabolic flux information. As the brain tissue metabolises ^{13}C-glucose, the labelled carbon is incorporated into specific carbon positions of brain amino-acid pools and we have been able to use this property to measure the kinetics of glucose utilisation. Carbon-13 is a stable isotope with a natural abundance of about 1%, which can be used as a very specific magnetic 'tag' attached to compounds of interest. The ^{13}C NMR method obtains NMR signals over a broader frequency range than the proton NMR technique and provides better resolution. Figure 1 (lower record) illustrates a human brain ^{13}C spectrum, showing signals from the methyl groups, from lipids in the skin and bone, from glycerol and from glucose. In the upper record, the spectrum was localised to the brain, enhancing the signals from the C_1 position of the α- and β-isomers of glucose.

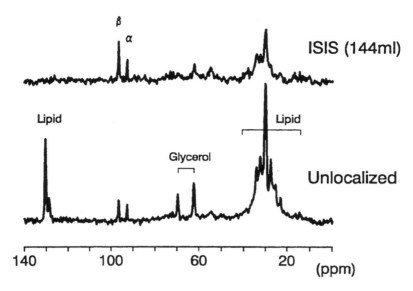

Figure 1 ^{13}Carbon NMR spectrum records from the brain. The lower record shows carbon signals from methyl groups, from lipids in the skin and bone, from glycerol and from glucose. For the upper record the scan was made under euglycaemic steady-state conditions, enhancing the signals from the C_1 position of the α and β enantiomers of glucose.

Again, one measurement was made during the hyperglycaemic step with isotopic fraction and the plasma glucose at steady state. Insulin was then infused to restore euglycaemia, and a second measurement made under isotopic steady-state conditions. From measurements of the isotopic fraction in plasma, the total glucose concentrations in the brain could then be calculated from a direct measurement of ^{13}C-glucose by NMR.

Overall, our experiments show that:

- the blood glucose concentration at which seizures and brain injury may result from hypoglycaemia is 1–2 mM
- at the hyperglycaemic step (12–18 mM), brain glucose concentrations may rise as high as 3.0 mM
- at the euglycaemic state (3–5 mM), brain glucose concentration is about 1.0 mM
- no significant differences in glucose transport kinetics were found between unaffected controls and patients with long standing hyperglycaemia due to poorly controlled diabetes (Novotny *et al.* 1995).

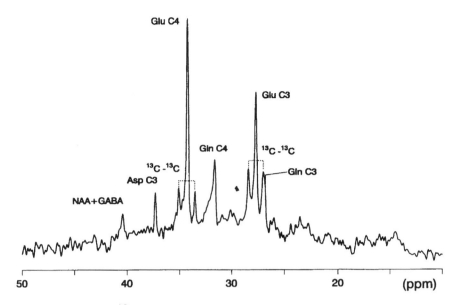

Figure 2 Three-hour ^{13}C NMR spectrum showing the ^{13}C signals from amino-acid pools as the brain metabolises ^{13}C glucose. ^{13}C has entered the C_3 and C_4 carbon positions of glutamate and glutamine, and the C_3 of aspartate.

NMRS studies using the natural abundant ^{13}C signal are relatively insensitive, although they have been used to measure glycogen content in the liver and muscles where the concentration is high (Shulman *et al.* 1990). The technique cannot be used in the brain, where none of the compounds to be studied are at a high enough ^{13}C concentration.

We have also optimised the ^{13}C NMR method to measure the rate of appearance of the ^{13}C signals from amino-acid pools as the brain metabolises ^{13}C glucose via glycolysis and the Krebs cycle to ketoglutarate and glutamate. The isotopic fraction in plasma was kept constant as the brain ^{13}C NMR measurements were being made at 4–5 minute intervals.

Figure 2 is the spectrum after 3 hours of ^{13}C glucose infusion. ^{13}C has entered the C_4 position of glutamate and carbon positions in other amino-acid pools, notably C_4 and C_3 in glutamine and aspartate, and also (shown in other studies) C_4 of γ-aminobutyric acid (GABA) (Gruetter *et al.* 1994, Manor *et al.* 1996). Computer modelling analyses have been used to determine specific metabolic flux rates in the brain from these data (Mason *et al.* 1995).

The Krebs cycle rate (glucose oxidation) can be determined from the rate of incorporation of ^{13}C into the glutamate C_4, and the glutamine synthesis

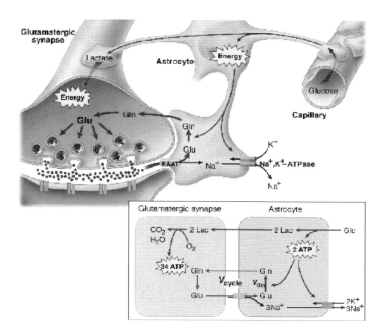

Figure 3 Astrocytes take up the excitatory neurotransmitter glutamate from the synaptic cleft, and metabolise it back to glutamine, which is taken up by the neuron for re-use.

rate is determined from the relative rates of incorporation into the glutamate C_4 and glutamine C_4 carbons. Glutamine synthesis rate provides a measure of baseline neuronal function. The latter is important to understand because glutamine synthesis occurs in astrocytes (where ammonia metabolism also primarily occurs) (Sibson *et al.* 1998, Magistretti *et al.* 1999). Astrocytes play the key role of taking up the excitatory neurotransmitter glutamate from the synaptic cleft, metabolising it back to glutamine that is taken up again into the neuron (Fig. 3).

^{13}C NMR data from control individuals in an early study showed a Krebs cycle rate of 0.73 ± 0.18 µmol/g/min, and glutamine synthesis rate of 0.47 µmol/g/min (Mason *et al.* 1995). These values correspond well with those found by positron emission tomography (PET) and other methods (Blomqvist *et al.* 1994).

Conclusions and future studies

- Non-invasive methods now exist to investigate glucose metabolism and hypoglycaemia in the immature brain.

- Further studies investigating the effects of hypoglycaemia on glia-neuronal metabolism and the synthesis and turnover of GABA and other neurotransmitters are in progress using NMR spectroscopy in children and adults.
- Studies of patients with genetic defects may show how abnormal enzymes and proteins that affect neurotransmitter pools, lead to long-term neurological handicaps.
- Further investigations using the ^{13}C-labelled compounds will be possible using not only glucose but also alternative energy substrates, particularly in the developing nervous system. These studies can determine the role of such substrates in energy metabolism and, most importantly, the potential prevention of hypoglycaemic brain injury in children.

References

Blomqvist G, Seitz RJ, Sjogren I , Halldin C, Stone-Elander S, Widen L *et al.* 1994 Regional cerebral oxidative and total glucose consumption during rest and activation studied with positron emission tomography. *Acta Physiologica Scandinavica* **151** 29–43.

Chugani HT, Phelps ME & Mazziotta JC 1987 Positron emission tomography study of human brain functional development. *Annals of Neurology* **22** 487–497.

Gruetter R, Novotny EJ, Boulware SD , Mason GF, Rothman DL, Shulman GI *et al.* 1994 Localized ^{13}C NMR spectroscopy in the human brain of amino acid labeling from D-[1–[13]C]glucose. *Journal of Neurochemistry* **63** 1377–1385.

Gruetter R, Novotny EJ, Boulware SD, Rothman DL & Shulman RG 1996 ^{1}H NMR studies of glucose transport in the human brain. *Journal of Cerebral Blood Flow and Metabolism* **16** 427–438.

Kinnala A, Suhonen-Polvi H, Aarimaa T, Kero P, Korvenranta H, Ruotsalainen U *et al.* 1996 Cerebral metabolic rate for glucose during the first six months of life: an FDG positron emission tomography study. *Archives of Diseases in Childhood, Fetal and Neonatal Edition* **74** F153–157.

Magistretti PJ, Pellerin L, Rothman DL & Shulman RG 1999 Energy on demand. *Science* **283** 496–497.

Manor D, Rothman DL, Mason GF, Hyder F, Petroff OA & Behar KL 1996 The rate of turnover of cortical GABA from [1–[13]C]glucose is reduced in rats treated with the GABA-transaminase inhibitor vigabatrin (gamma-vinyl GABA). *Neurochemical Research* **21** 1031–1041.

Mason GF, Gruetter R, Rothman DL, Behar KL, Shulman RG & Novotny EJ 1995 Simultaneous determination of the rates of the TCA cycle glucose utilization alpha-ketoglutarate/glutamate exchange and glutamine synthesis in human brain by NMR. *Journal of Cerebral Blood Flow and Metabolism* **15** 12–25.

Nehlig A & Pereira de Vasconcelos A 1993 Glucose and ketone body utilization by the brain of neonatal rats. *Progress in Neurobiology* **40** 163–221.

Novotny EJ, Gruetter R, Rothman DL, Boulware S, Tamborlane WV & Shulman RG 1995 Chronic hyperglycemia does not alter steady-state human brain glucose concentrations: a ^{13}C NMR study. *Annals of Neurology* **34** 467–468.

Novotny E, Ashwal S & Shevell M 1998 Proton magnetic resonance spectroscopy: an emerging technology in pediatric neurology research. *Pediatric Research* **44** 1–10.

Shulman GI, Rothman DL, Jue T, Stein P, DeFronzo RA & Shulman RG 1990 Quantitation of muscle glycogen synthesis in normal subjects and subjects with non-insulin-dependent diabetes by ^{13}C nuclear magnetic resonance spectroscopy. *New England Journal of Medicine* **322** 223–228.

Sibson NR, Shen J, Mason GF, Rothman DL, Behar KL & Shulman RG 1998 Functional energy metabolism: in vivo ^{13}C-NMR spectroscopy evidence for coupling of cerebral glucose consumption and glutamatergic neuronal activity. *Developmental Neuroscience* **20** 321–330.

Vannucci SJ, Seaman LB, Brucklacher RM and Vannucci RC 1994 Glucose transport in developing rat brain: glucose transporter proteins rate constants and cerebral glucose utilization. *Molecular and Cellular Biochemistry* **140** 177–84.

Genetic Insights in Paediatric Endocrinology and Metabolism
Eds S O'Rahilly and D B Dunger
BioScientifica Ltd, Bristol (1999)

Genetic disorders of the pituitary–thyroid axis

V K K Chatterjee

University of Cambridge Department of Medicine, Level 5, Addenbrooke's Hospital, Hills Road, Cambridge CB2 2QQ, UK

We present the results of research into inherited thyroid disorders – with particular emphasis on resistance to thyroid hormone (RTH), together with genetically defined cases of congenital hypothyroidism (CH).

Human thyroid hormones

Thyroid hormones (THs) regulate processes as diverse as growth, the basal metabolic rate (BMR), myocardial contractility and development of the central nervous system. The synthesis of thyroxine (T4) and triiodothyronine (T3) in the thyroid is governed by thyrotropin-releasing hormone (TRH) from the hypothalamus and thyroid-stimulating hormone (TSH) from the pituitary; the THs in turn inhibit TSH secretion as part of a negative feedback loop (Fig. 1).

In addition, THs exert important affects on other target tissues – some of which are readily quantified (Fig. 1, Table 1).

Table 1 Effects of THs on other target tissues

Metabolism	BMR
Liver	sex hormone binding globulin (SHBG) levels
Heart	rate and contractility
Skeleton	linear growth in children; bone mineral density (BMD) in adults
Brain	in-utero and postnatal development

The thyroid hormone receptor

In 1986, two groups from the Salk and Karolinska Institutes reported that the cellular homologue of the viral oncogene *v-erbA* is the nuclear receptor

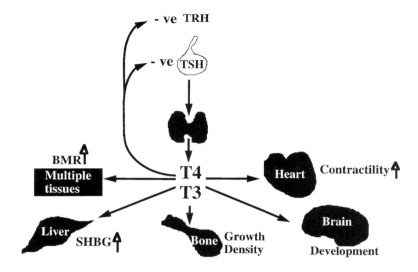

Figure 1 Major effects of thyroid hormones. Thyroid hormones exert many effects. Synthesis of T4 and T3 in the thyroid is governed by TRH from the hypothalamus and TSH from the pituitary. THs in turn control TRH and TSH secretion by negative feedback. THs also regulate many other physiological processes.

designated TR. The actions of TH are mediated through TR, which is a member of the nuclear receptor family of ligand-inducible transcription factors that also includes the steroid, vitamin D and retinoid receptors. The TR proteins are organised in a modular fashion. A central zinc-finger domain mediates binding to specific DNA sequences (thyroid response elements, TREs) in target gene promoters to regulate their transcription in a hormone-dependent manner. A carboxy-terminal domain mediates occupancy by the cognate ligand; the function of the amino-terminal region is less well understood.

It is now recognised that practically all the effects of TH on many body systems are mediated by the modulation of target gene expression, and the current model of how TR exerts its effects on gene transcription is summarised in Fig. 2. This model is based on an enormous body of research by many groups worldwide undertaken since the cloning of the receptor (Lazar 1993). TR occupies its TRE in a target gene, typically as a heterodimer with a partner molecule, the retinoid X receptor (RXR). In the absence of TH (Fig. 2, upper), this heterodimer binds a complex of other proteins including transcriptional corepressors (either SMRT or NcoR). The corepressor mediates interaction with the protein Sin3 which recruits

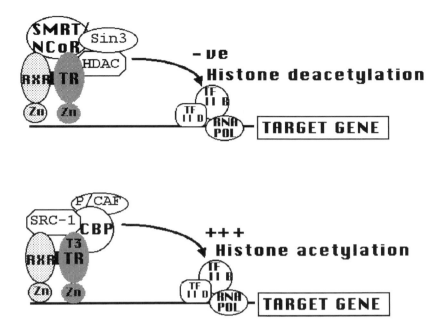

Figure 2 Current model of positive transcriptional regulation by thyroid hormone. The TR-RXR heterodimer occupies a specific DNA binding site (TRE) on the target gene. **Upper:** in the absence of T3, it binds a complex of proteins including corepressor which deacetylates histones in chromatin, silencing gene transcription. **Lower:** T3 occupancy promotes corepressor dissociation followed by recruitment of a coactivator complex and leads to histone acetylation, allowing enhanced target gene transcription and mRNA synthesis.

histone deacetylase (HDAC). The net effect is that the complex mediates deacetylation of histones in chromatin, allowing tighter binding of DNA to core histones, preventing access by basal transcription factors thereby silencing gene transcription. Conversely, following receptor occupancy by T3 (Fig. 2, lower), the corepressor complex dissociates and alternative proteins, the coactivators, are recruited; these include steroid-receptor coactivator SRC-1, cyclic AMP response-binding protein (CBP) and the accessory factor P/CAF. Many or all of these proteins have the opposite function to that of HDAC – they acetylate histones within chromatin. Thus it appears that the presence of TH, causing recruitment of the coactivator complex, leads to histone acetylation and relaxation of the binding of DNA to core histones; this allows access of basal transcription factors and RNA polymerase to DNA, leading to enhanced target gene transcription and mRNA synthesis. This scheme generally holds true for all genes which are induced (i.e. positively regulated) by TR.

The syndrome of resistance to thyroid hormone (RTH)

RTH is usually dominantly inherited and the 'biochemical signature' by which patients with this disorder are recognised includes elevated circulating free T3 and T4 levels combined with an inappropriately normal TSH level. The TSH is neither suppressed as would be expected in thyrotoxicosis nor (usually) abnormally raised, and peripheral target tissues exhibit variable refractoriness to TH. Soon after the cloning of TR, a group at the NIH showed that RTH was tightly linked to the TRβ gene locus on chromosome 3 (Usala *et al.* 1988). It is now recognised that there are two TR genes in humans (α, β) which undergo alternate splicing to generate highly homologous receptor isoforms (TRα1, TRα2, TRβ1, TRβ2) with different tissue distributions. TRα1 is found mainly in the heart, skeletal muscle and CNS; TRα2 does not bind T3 and its function is poorly understood. TRβ1 is expressed in many tissues, whilst TRβ2 is highly expressed in the liver, pituitary and hypothalamus. We and other groups have identified about 400 families with the syndrome of RTH. The mode of inheritance in all but one family is autosomal dominant and individuals are heterozygous for mutations of the receptor gene. All defects so far identified are localised to the hormone binding domain of the β receptor and so affect both the β1 and β2 gene products (Refetoff *et al.* 1993, Chatterjee *et al.* 1998). Consequently, the functional defect most often seen is the failure to bind ligand normally, leading to impaired transcriptional activity of the receptor.

Insights from molecular studies of RTH mutants

For example, in studies of hormone-dependent repression of the human TSHα gene promoter, each mutant receptor studied showed a right-shifted response profile relative to that of the wild type receptor, with increasing concentrations of T3. Mutants with a partial defect in binding attained a wild type level of function if exposed to a high enough T3 concentration, but more deleterious mutants never achieved normal function (Collingwood *et al.* 1994). We have also shown that when coexpressed in a transfected cell, all the dysfunctional mutant receptors inhibit the function of wild type receptor in a dominant negative manner (Collingwood *et al.* 1994). The proposed mechanism for this effect is as follows. In the absence of T3, the wild type receptor heterodimer binds the corepressors and silences gene transcription, whilst in its presence the corepressors dissociate, as described above. However, because the mutant receptor fails to bind T3, it remains constitutively associated with the corepressors and silences the target gene. These mutant receptor complexes compete with the wild type complexes for access to target gene TREs. This model predicts that three functional properties are preserved in mutant receptors: the ability to bind to DNA; to heterodimerise with RXR; and to bind corepressors. All have been experimentally verified for many natural mutants (Collingwood *et al.* 1994). Conversely, dominant negative activity can be abrogated by the introduction of artificial mutations that disrupt DNA binding heterodimerisation or corepressor interaction (Collingwood *et al.* 1994, Yoh *et al.* 1997).

The study of natural RTH mutants has helped map structure–function relationships within TR. The crystal structure of the hormone binding domain of TR in the presence of T3 has been elucidated (Wagner *et al.* 1995) and we have shown that most mutations cluster round the hormone binding cavity whilst helices 1 (mediating corepressor interaction) and 9 and 10 (dimerisation) are devoid of mutations (Collingwood *et al.* 1998). Most recently we have described natural receptor mutants with altered cofactor recruitment. Mutations in helices 3 and 12 selectively abolish coactivator binding and may delineate a possible receptor–coactivator interface.

Some RTH mutations have shown enhanced binding of corepressor and, in one (R383H), corepressor release and negative transcriptional regulation were both selectively impaired. The transcriptional properties of the R383H mutant on a reporter gene that is positively regulated (induced) by T3 are indistinguishable from those of wild type receptor but, with negatively regulated promoters such as hypothalamic TRH or pituitary TSHα/β, there are small but clear differences between mutant and wild type. So, functionally this mutant is selectively impaired for negative, but not positive regulation of target genes. Transcriptional profiles show that, in the absence of T3, both wild type and R383H mutant TR enhance basal activity of the negatively regulated TRH gene promoter to the same extent. With increasing T3 concentrations, this enhanced promoter activity is gradually reversed with wild type receptor, whilst the R383H mutant shows impaired inhibition of promoter activity (Clifton-Bligh *et al.* 1998). Furthermore, hormone-dependent dissociation of receptor from corepressor is slightly impaired with the R383H mutant, whereas hormone-dependent recruitment of coactivator is normal. The properties of this subtle natural mutant tell us that impairment of negative transcriptional regulation –

together with an abnormal interaction between the receptor and corepressor – may be the minimum functional abnormalities needed to cause RTH.

Another receptor mutation (L454V) was found in individuals with very high TH levels (free T4 ≥80 pmol/l; comparable with those seen in Graves' disease). Although this mutant can bind T3 as effectively as the wild type receptor, its transcriptional ability is severely impaired, even at T3 concentrations as high as 1 μM (Collingwood *et al.* 1997). The cause of this disparity is the relative inability of the mutant to interact with coactivator SRC-1. Accordingly, L454V mutant receptor function can be rescued by cotransfecting SRC-1 coactivator. Comparable rescue of its function is also possible with negatively regulated genes (hypothalamic TRH and TSH).

Thus, the properties of the R383H and L454V receptor mutants allow us to extend the model of TR action (Fig. 3). For positively-regulated genes (Fig. 3, upper), in the absence of T3, the receptor binds corepressor leading

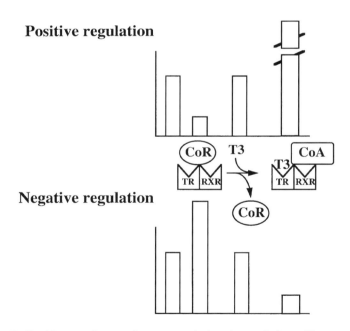

Figure 3 Positive and negative transcriptional regulation. **Upper:** for positively regulated genes, in the absence of T3, the receptor binds corepressor leading to silencing of transcription; T3 causes derepression, coactivator recruitment and true activation of transcription. **Lower:** for negatively regulated genes the opposite occurs. In the absence of T3, binding to the corepressor complex leads to activation of basal transcription; the presence of T3 triggers dissociation of corepressors and reversal of this, but true negative transcriptional regulation also requires the recruitment of coactivator.

to silencing of transcription; T3 binding causes derepression, followed by coactivator recruitment and activation of transcription. We believe that for negatively regulated genes (Fig. 3, lower) the opposite occurs. In the absence of T3, the receptor–corepressor complex mediates basal transcriptional activation; the presence of T3 triggers dissociation of corepressors and reversal of basal activation, but true negative transcriptional regulation also requires recruitment of coactivators. Thus, studies on RTH are elucidating the roles of coactivators and corepressors in the negative feedback regulation of hypothalamic and pituitary target genes.

Clinical features of RTH

Our cohort of patients with RTH is the largest in the world (more than 100 families). Clinical studies on the peripheral markers of TH action in these patients show that: SHBG levels are generally within the normal range (Beck-Peccoz & Chatterjee 1994); BMR may be elevated and body mass index decreased, particularly in children, suggesting that not all tissues are completely refractory to TH (Matthews, CH and Chatterjee, VKK, unpublished data); cardiac indices (e.g. isovolumetric relaxation time, minute volume index) are abnormal and qualitatively similar to values seen in patients with thyrotoxicosis (Kahaly *et al.* 1998).

Thus, a complex clinical picture of the RTH syndrome is emerging (Fig. 4). All patients have a detectable TSH level, indicating central (hypothalamic and pituitary) resistance to TH, and most appear to have liver resistance (normal SHBG). However, some peripheral sensitivity to TH is retained such that thyrotoxic cardiac problems often manifest and the basal metabolic rate is sometimes elevated. Such variable tissue resistance is partly due to the fact that the myocardium and skeletal muscle predominantly express TRα, whereas the pituitary, hypothalamus and liver express relatively more TRβ isoforms. However, we await the development of an animal model of RTH before the genetic basis of clinical phenotypic variability can be fully determined.

Congenital hypothyroidism (CH)

CH affects approximately 1/4000 of live births and, if untreated, results in major impairment in the development of the central nervous system. Our research suggests that TSH receptor (TSHR) mutations can cause either partially compensated or severe hypothyroidism presenting neonatally. A child detected by the neonatal hypothyroidism screening programme in

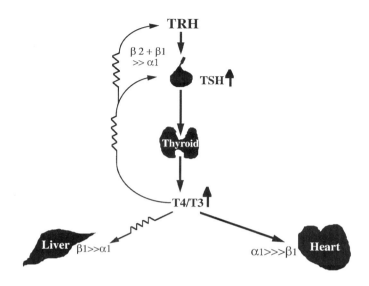

Figure 4 The complex clinical picture of RTH. All patients have detectable TSH (and so central resistance to TH) and most have liver resistance (normal SHBG) but some tissues retain sensitivity to elevated TH accounting for elevated BMR and cardiac thyrotoxic features. Such variable resistance is partly due to predominance of TRα expression in skeletal muscle and myocardium and TRβ expression in liver, pituitary and hypothalamus.

Cardiff, UK, with a high TSH level of about 100 mU/l and a free thyroxine level of just below the reference range (approx. 10 pmol/l) became hyperactive on thyroxine replacement as his free T4 rose above normal and the TSH came down. His symptoms resolved on stopping thyroxine treatment. The thyroid gland was normal in size and location. It emerged that this child is a compound heterozygote for two different loss-of-function mutations in the TSH receptor (TSHR) (Clifton-Bligh *et al.* 1997). Two other children we studied had elevated TSH and very low TH levels on neonatal screening. Unexpectedly, both were found to be compound heterozygous for loss-of-function mutations in the TSHR. Different TSHR mutations have also been found in members of another family with markedly raised TSH and very low T4 (Abramowicz *et al.* 1997).

Thyroid agenesis and the role of thyroid transcription factor 2

Thyroid agenesis (or dysgenesis) is responsible for the vast majority of cases of CH. The embryonic development of the thyroid from a medial pharyngeal anlage and its descent to its final position are accompanied by the expression of thyroid-specific transcription factors (TTFs) such as TTF-1, PAX-8 and TTF-2. We studied two male siblings with CH due to thyroid agenesis who also have cleft palate, choanal atresia and spiky hair (Bamforth *et al.* 1989). TTF-2 is a transcription factor belonging to the forkhead domain family which is highly expressed in the developing thyroid gland. We found that both siblings are homozygous for a missense (alanine to valine) mutation in the forkhead domain of TTF-2 which abolishes its DNA binding and transcriptional functions (Clifton-Bligh *et al.* 1998). The clinical phenotype in these patients is strikingly similar to that of mice in which the TTF-2 gene has been experimentally disrupted (De Felice *et al.* 1998). Our observations suggest that TTF-2 plays an important role in thyroid development and also mediates developmental effects in extrathyroidal tissues.

Conclusions and future directions

- The identification of TR and transcriptional cofactors – corepressors and coactivators – are important steps in understanding the control of TH action in many physiological processes.
- Our studies of the genetic syndrome of RTH are providing clinical and molecular insights into how TH exerts its effects on target genes and tissues.
- Future studies may identify defects in cofactor genes causing unusual forms of RTH. An animal model will facilitate fuller understanding of the phenotypic variability of this disorder.
- Defects in thyroid transcription factors (TTF-1, TTF-2, PAX-8) result in thyroid dysgenesis associated with developmental anomalies in other organs systems, because the transcription factors control many downstream target genes, not only in the thyroid but also in other tissues.
- However, future analyses of downstream target genes in the thyroid may lead to the identification of the defects leading solely to thyroid agenesis – the commonest cause of CH.

References

Abramowicz MJ, Duprez L, Parma J, Vassart G & Heinrichs C 1997 Familial congenital hypothyroidism due to inactivating mutation of the thyrotropin receptor causing profound hypoplasia of the thyroid gland. *Journal of Clinical Investigation* **99** 3018–3024.

Bamforth JS, Hughes IA, Lazarus JH, Weaver CM & Harper PS 1989 Congenital hypothyroidism, spiky hair, and cleft palate. *Journal of Medical Genetics* **26** 49–51.

Beck Peccoz P & Chatterjee VKK 1994 The variable clinical phenotype in thyroid hormone resistance syndrome. *Thyroid* **4** 225–232.

Chatterjee VKK, Clifton-Bligh RJ & Gurnell M 1998 Thyroid hormone resistance. In *Contemporary Endocrinology: Hormone Resistance Syndromes*, pp 145–163. Ed JL Jameson. New Jersey: Humana Press.

Clifton-Bligh R J, de Zegher F, Wagner RL *et al.* 1998 A novel TRβ mutation (R383H) in resistance to thyroid hormone predominantly impairs corepressor release and negative transcriptional regulation. *Molecular Endocrinology* **12** 609–621.

Clifton-Bligh RJ, Gregory JW, Ludgate M *et al.* 1997 Two novel mutations in the thyrotropin (TSH) receptor gene in a child with resistance to TSH. *Journal of Clinical Endocrinology and Metabolism* **82** 1094–1100.

Clifton-Bligh RJ, Wentworth JM, Heinz P *et al.* 1998. Mutation of the gene encoding human TTF-2 associated with thyroid agenesis, cleft palate and choanal atresia. *Nature Genetics* **19** 399–401.

Collingwood TN, Adams M, Tone Y & Chatterjee VKK. 1994 Spectrum of transcriptional dimerization and dominant negative properties of twenty different mutant thyroid hormone β receptors in thyroid hormone resistance syndrome. *Molecular Endocrinology* **8** 1262–1277.

Collingwood TN, Rajanayagam O, Adams O *et al.* 1997 A natural transactivation mutation in the thyroid hormone β receptor: impaired interaction with putative transcriptional mediators. *Proceedings of the National Academy of Science, USA* **94** 248–253.

Collingwood TN, Wagner R, Matthews CH *et al.* 1998 A role of helix 3 of the TRβ ligand binding domain in coactivator recruitment identified by characterization of a third cluster of mutations in resistance to thyroid hormone. *EMBO Journal* **17** 4760–4770.

De Felice M, Ovitt C, Biffali E *et al.* 1998 A mouse model for hereditary thyroid dysgenesis and cleft palate. *Nature Genetics* **19** 395–398.

Kahaly GJ, Matthews CH, Mohr-Kahaly S, Richards C, Rippin G & Chatterjee VKK 1998 Cardiac investigation in resistance to thyroid hormone. *71st Annual Meeting of the American Thyroid Association*, p 69. Portland, Oregon: The American Thyroid Association, Inc.

Lazar MA 1993 Thyroid hormone receptors: multiple forms, multiple possibilities. *Endocrine Reviews* **14** 184–193.

Refetoff S, Weiss RE & Usala SJ 1993 The syndromes of resistance to thyroid hormone. *Endocrine Reviews* **14** 348–399.

Usala SJ, Bale AE, Gesundheit N *et al.* 1988. Tight linkage between the syndrome of generalized thyroid hormone resistance and the human c-erbA β gene. *Molecular Endocrinology* **2** 1217–1220.

Wagner RL, Apriletti JW, McGrath ME, West BL, Baxter JD & Fletterick RJ 1995 A structural role for hormone in the thyroid hormone receptor. *Nature* **378** 690–697.

Yoh SM, Chatterjee VKK & Privalsky ML 1997 Thyroid hormone resistance syndrome manifests as an aberrant interaction between mutant T3 receptors and transcriptional corepressors. *Molecular Endocrinology* **11** 470–480.

Diabetes

Genetic Insights in Paediatric Endocrinology and Metabolism
Eds S O'Rahilly and D B Dunger
BioScientifica Ltd, Bristol (1999)

Insulin resistance syndromes

S O'Rahilly

Addenbrookes Hospital, Hills Road, Cambridge CB2 2QQ, UK

Insulin resistance is associated with many conditions, from the relatively few individuals affected by rare syndromes to the vast numbers who suffer from obesity. Here are reviewed individual cases involving insulin resistance that illustrate the genetic basis of defective insulin action, its consequences for human disease and what is being learnt from studying syndromes of insulin resistance.

Insulin resistance and disease

The rare syndromes characterised by insulin resistance are usually monogenic, and a primary defect in insulin action is thought to underlie all the phenotypic abnormalities (Taylor 1992). Insulin resistance contributes – probably causally – to non-insulin-dependent diabetes mellitus (NIDDM) and hypertension and is also a feature of polycystic ovary syndrome and the constellation of cardiovascular risk factors known as syndrome X. Obesity is the commonest condition in which insulin resistance is found.

Severe insulin resistance syndromes

Features of the syndromes of severe insulin resistance include: resistance to the metabolic action of insulin in specific tissues (e.g. liver, muscle, fat); secondary effects of the gross hyperinsulinaemia that results from this; and features specific to each syndrome. Impaired glucose tolerance or diabetes usually results from the massive hyperinsulinaemia, but normoglycaemia may be maintained for a remarkably long time and hypoglycaemia can sometimes occur even when insulin receptors are absent. The secondary effects of hyperinsulinaemia include ovarian hyperandrogenism and the skin condition, acanthosis nigricans. The cause of acanthosis nigricans is still unknown. Excess insulin may stimulates skin insulin-like growth factor-I (IGF-1) receptors and causes the abnormal skin growth, but the condition is rare in true acromegaly, in which excess IGF-1 is present.

Syndromes of severe insulin resistance can conveniently be classified as genetic or acquired (Table 1).

Table 1 Syndromes of severe insulin resistance

Genetic syndromes
      Donahue's syndrome (leprechaunism), Rabson–Mendenhall syndrome, type A insulin resistance
      HAIR-AN, insulin resistance with pseudoacromegaly
      Congenital lipodystrophy, face-sparing lipodystrophy
      Alström's syndrome, mandibulo-acral dysplasia etc.
Acquired syndromes
      Type B insulin resistance
      Acquired lipodystrophies

HAIR-AN, hyperandrogenism, insulin resistance and acanthosis nigricans

Among genetic syndromes, Donahue's and Rabson–Mendenhall are the classic insulin-receptor defect syndromes, and type A insulin resistance, occurring particularly in slim females, is commonly caused by insulin receptor mutations. A second group of syndromes combine insulin resistance with moderate obesity and features of polycystic ovary syndrome, or acromegaly-like changes in the extremities. Autosomal recessive lipodystrophies, and pleotropic syndromes such as Alström's, form two further groups. In the latter group, insulin resistance is only one component of a complex genetic disorder.

Acquired syndromes include type B insulin resistance – a very rare autoimmune disorder involving antibodies to the insulin receptor and associated with lymphomas and systemic lupus erythematosus – and acquired lipodystrophies, which are probably also autoimmune in type.

Why study rare syndromes?

The study of these rare conditions is important for several reasons. First, the disorders are of themselves extremely serious and distressing diseases, with high morbidity and early mortality, which may benefit from genetic counselling at least and rational therapy at most. Secondly, their study also has the potential to provide insights into the normal biology of insulin action in humans, and thirdly they can provide models of, and ways of thinking about, the more common disorders of insulin action.

Insulin receptor signalling pathways

Up to about ten years ago, the enzymes involved in the metabolism of glucose into lipid and glycogen, and the insulin receptor itself, were quite

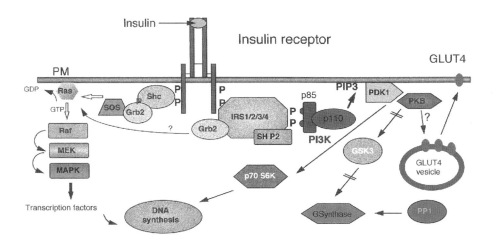

Figure 1 The insulin receptor is a transmembrane tyrosine kinase. Upon insulin binding, critical tyrosine residues within the intracellular β-subunits of the receptor are autophosphorylated. The kinase function of the receptor towards downstream substrates is thereby released and a number of such substrates phosphorylated on tyrosine residues. These include members of the insulin receptor substrate (IRS) family and the smaller intracellular adapter molecule shc. Activation of IRS-1-associated phosphatidylinositol 3-kinase is thought to be central to initiation of metabolic signalling, whilsethe growth factor effects of insulin, which it shares with other receptors, are likely to involve the ras/raf/map kinase cascade.

well understood. But very little was known about the signal transduction molecules between the receptor and the downstream effectors of insulin action. An explosion of information about insulin signalling pathways (Fig. 1) has appeared since then (White 1997, Czech & Corvera 1999).

Like the platelet-derived and epidermal growth factor (PDGF, EGF) receptors, the insulin receptor is a transmembrane receptor tyrosine kinase (TK), but it differs from them in several key aspects. First, it is not dimerised by ligand, but is constitutively dimerised by disulphide bonds. Secondly, the first target is a tyrosine residue within the kinase domain, and this autophosphorylation event is crucial for the transmission downstream of the kinase signal. In contrast, the autophosphorylation sites on the EGF receptor are not necessary for TK activity. Finally, when the EGF receptor becomes autophosphorylated it attracts to the membrane a range of proteins containing SH_2 domains that 'dock' at a the plasma membrane, and this acts as the major source for the mitogenic signalling of the receptor; but the insulin receptor phosphorylates soluble molecules which then can move within the cytosol and act at a distal compartment. These may be critically

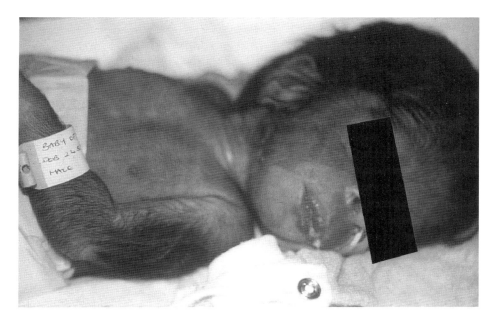

Figure 2 A male infant with the typical features of Donahue's syndrome (leprechaunism): growth retardation, severe hirsutism and an extremely high plasma insulin level (64 000 pmol/litre). A homozygously transmitted mutation resulted in complete absence of insulin receptors (receptor null phenotype).

important for the translocation of glucose vesicles to the cell surface in response to insulin.

The insulin receptor phosphorylates a tyrosine site on the insulin receptor substrate-1 (IRS-1) molecule, and the phosphotyrosine site can then interact with a range of proteins carrying SH_2 docking domains. Several third-level events then occur. A consensus is emerging that the action of insulin on phosphatidylinositol (PI) 3-kinase is central to its rapid effects on metabolic events. However, the activity of insulin as a growth factor is probably mediated by the raf, RAS and map kinase pathways. It is not clear whether this is mediated largely by SHC or IRS-1, but the former is more probable.

Insulin receptor defect syndromes

The gene for the insulin receptor is very large, consisting of 22 exons extending over 150 kb of DNA. During the last few years, my colleagues and I have used molecular scanning to identify many mutations of the insulin receptor, some of which are described below.

Homozygous insulin receptor mutations

The infant shown in Fig. 2 was born to consanguineous parents of Pakistani origin at a weight of 1.6 kg at 36 weeks gestation. He had typical features of Donahue's syndrome (leprechaunism) with severe hirsutism and the highest plasma insulin concentration we had ever measured: 64 000 pmol/litre. Both parents carried a heterozygous lysine-to-stop-codon mutation, and the infant's diagnosis was confirmed post mortem by PCR of DNA recovered from a heel-prick blood sample taken at birth.

This mutation placed the stop codon in exon 2, well before the transmembrane domain, resulting in the first recorded example of the insulin receptor null phenotype. It had been thought that insulin action was needed for normal development from an early fetal stage, but, although growth was impaired in this child, central nervous stystem development was normal even in the total absence of receptors. It seems that the very high concentrations of insulin were acting on related receptors and conducting some of the biological activities of insulin (Krook *et al.* 1993).

A highly growth-retarded male patient developed diabetes at 6 years and even up to 10 000 U of insulin/day did not full restore normoglycaemia. By 18 years, he was blind due to diabetic retinopathy, in renal failure, and had foot ulcers which developed sepsis and led to a bilateral above-the-knee amputation following which he died at 21 years. The insulin resistance in this patient was due to homozygosity for a missense mutation in the extracellular domain of the insulin receptor (Krook *et al.* 1996).

Receptors were present, but failed to bind insulin because of the defective conformation. We were able to correct the conformation and restore function in the defective receptors on stably transfected cells by treatment with a divalent monoclonal antibody to the extracellular domain; levels of glycogen synthesis close to those of the wild-type receptor were detected.

Heterozygous insulin receptor mutations

Both the preceding patients were homozygous for insulin receptor mutations. Their parents were almost normoglycaemic and normo-insulinaemic, despite being heterozygotes with a 50% loss of insulin receptors. However, some receptor mutations cause insulin resistance even in the heterozygous form.

Two of these – Arg1174Gln and Pro1178Leu – were found in girls with typical features of type A insulin resistance. They were dominantly inherited and occurred in the catalytic loop of the kinase domain, where they were predicted to cause major disruption of tight turns in the kinase. Neither autophosphorylation nor kinase reactions were detected; the kinase domain in both subunits of the receptor must function for normal signalling and internalisation to follow insulin stimulation (Krook *et al*. 1997).

In one family, another Arg1174 mutation occurred – Arg1174Trp, in which heterozygotes are practically normal, in contrast to the insulin resistance found in heterozygotes with Arg1174Gln. We found that, paradoxically, more severely impaired receptors may actually lead to a milder phenotype, because they are selectively degraded and so do not interfere with the action of any remaining normal receptors. Hence the mildness or severity of a mutation and the clinical phenotype are not necessarily positively correlated (unpublished observations).

Post-receptor mutations

A female patient presenting with type A insulin resistance, NIDDM, dyslipidaemia, hypertension, hirsutism and acanthosis nigricans has a Met613Val mutation in the IRS-1 gene which was not found in unaffected family members or in 200 normal alleles. The mutation occurs in a highly conserved YMXM motif that has the highest affinity for PI 3-kinase (Fig. 1). A mutant synthetic peptide was very poorly phosphorylated by the insulin receptor. Confusingly it appeared to recruit PI 3-kinase quite normally, but was less able than the normal peptide to interact with GRB2, suggesting that GRB2 may be closely involved in insulin's metabolic action (Whitehead *et al*. 1998).

Pseudoacromegalic phenotype

In patients with this phenotype, insulin resistance is combined with typical acromegaloid changes (e.g. increased hand size, macroglossia, soft tissue thickening). In these patients insulin can stimulate amino-acid transport but not glucose transport, and these features persist in cultured fibroblasts. The ability of 1 nM insulin to activate PI 3-kinase is consistently and highly significantly lowered by about 70%.

The lesion responsible for this has not yet been precisely located. However, our model for the development of pseudoacromegaly proposes that a mutation at a post-receptor site leads to excessive serum insulin levels, but that these cannot activate the metabolic insulin pathways. However, insulin acting through a competent receptor can activate mitogenesis, as those pathways remain intact (Dib *et al*. 1998).

Table 2 Insulin-like peptides and syndromes of excessive growth

Syndrome	Cause	Consequences
IGF-1 mediated		
Acromegaly	Pituitary tumour	↑GH → ↑IGF-1
	Islet-cell tumour	↑GRF → ↑GH → ↑IGF-1
IGF-2 mediated		
Beckwith-Wiedemann and related syndromes	Loss of imprinting of IGF-2 gene	↑IGF-2
Tumoral IGF production	Fibrosarcoma binding to IGFBPs	Impaired IGF-2 → ↑free IGF-2
Insulin mediated		
Insulin resistant pseudoacromegaly	Selective post-receptor insulin resistance	↑Insulin

GH, growth hormone; IGF, insulin-like growth factor; GRF, growth-hormone releasing factor; IGFBP, insulin-like growth factor binding protein.

Overgrowth syndromes

Table 2 summarises the role of insulin-like peptides, and probably of insulin itself, in the pathogenesis of syndromes of excessive growth.

Conclusions and the future

- Donahue's and Rabson–Mendenhall syndrome are associated with severe defects in the insulin receptor, and research into therapy for these devastating disorders is a priority.
- The great number of molecules involved in post-receptor signalling defects makes investigation very difficult. Our own group is currently studying about 40 candidate genes from 150 patients with severe insulin resistance, in collaboration with a well-equipped biotechnology group.
- Alström's syndrome should soon be understood, as it is a monogenic disorder.
- The link between insulin resistance, lipodystrophy and obesity will be the subject of intensive research in the near future.
- Insulin resistance is associated with the presence of both too many and too few fat cells; the most likely explanation for this is that a primary defect causes lipodystrophy or obesity, which then leads to insulin resistance. Knowledge of the molecular basis of the lipodystrophies will

soon lead to enormous advances in our understanding of why the defect causes insulin resistance.

• The Dunnigan–Kobberling syndrome is characterised by fat loss in limbs but not the omental depot or face. In all families so far described, this is a completely monogenic homogeneous condition linking to a small region of chromosome 1q. This syndrome will provide an extremely useful monogenic model for investigating syndrome X (Peters *et al.* 1998, Jackson *et al.* 1998).

References

Czech MP & Corvera S 1999 Signaling mechanisms that regulate glucose transport. *Journal of Biological Chemistry* **274** 1865–1868.

Dib K, Whitehead JP, Humphreys PJ *et al.* 1998 Impaired activation of PI3-kinase by insulin fibroblasts from patients with severe insulin resistance and pseudo-acromegaly: a disorder characterised by selective post-receptor insulin resistance. *Journal of Clinical Investigation* **101** 1111–1120.

Jackson SNJ, Pinkney J & Bargiotta A 1998 A defect in the regional deposition of adipose tissue (partial lipodystrophy) is encoded by a gene at chromosome 1q. *American Journal of Human Genetics* **63** 534–540.

Krook A, Brueton L & O'Rahilly S 1993 Homozygous nonsense mutation in the insulin receptor gene in infant with leprechaunism. *Lancet* **342** 277–278.

Krook A, Soos M, Kumar S, Siddle K & O'Rahilly S 1996. Functional activation of mutant insulin receptor by monoclonal antibody. *Lancet* **347** 1586–1590.

Krook A, Whitehead JP, Dobson SP *et al.* 1997. Two naturally occurring mutations in the insulin receptor tyrosine kinase domain provide evidence that pI3-kinase activation alone is insufficient for the mediation of the metabolic effects of insulin. *Journal of Biological Chemistry* **272** 30208–30214.

Peters JM, Barnes R, Bennett L, Gitomer WM, Bowcock AM & Garg A 1998 Localization of the gene for familial partial lipodystrophy (Dunnigan variety) to chromosome 1q21-22. *Nature Genetics* **18** 292–295.

Taylor SI 1992 Lilly lecture – molecular mechanisms of insulin resistance – lessons from patients with mutations in the insulin-receptor gene. *Diabetes* **41** 1473–1490.

White MF 1997 The insulin signalling system and the IRS proteins. *Diabetologica* **40** (suppl.) S2–S17.

Whitehead JP, Humphreys P & Krook A 1998 Molecular scanning of the insulin receptor substrate 1 gene in subjects with severe insulin resistance: detection and functional analysis of a naturally occurring mutation in a YMXM motif. *Diabetes* **47** 837–839.

Genetic Insights in Paediatric Endocrinology and Metabolism
Eds S O'Rahilly and D B Dunger
BioScientifica Ltd, Bristol (1999)

Treatment options for severe insulin resistance

A Moses
Harvard Medical School, Joslin Diabetes Center, One Joslin Place, Boston
MA 02215, USA

Insulin resistance is now known to contribute to the underlying pathology of a host of common medical conditions as diverse as hypertension and type 2 diabetes mellitus, as described in the preceding chapter. An abnormality of any one of the pathways involved in insulin signalling or insulin action, at the extra-, trans- or intracellular level can result in insulin resistance and in one of the several clinical phenotypes of severe insulin resistance. The range of potential treatments for severe insulin resistance is limited but some established therapeutic approaches are discussed here, together with emerging therapeutic approaches for type 2 diabetes that may help patients with severe insulin resistance.

Insulin functions and insulin resistance

Insulin is generally thought of as the hormone that affects muscle, adipose tissue and liver to increase glucose uptake, to inhibit lipolysis or to inhibit hepatic production or output of glucose, respectively. However, insulin receptors are also expressed in the skin, brain, ovary, kidney and vascular system, and the normal physiological functions of insulin in these tissues are much less well understood (Fig. 1). In some cases, 'persistent' insulin action in these tissues appears to contribute to the phenotype of severe insulin resistance.

In addition, the range of different phenotypes seen in patients who present with insulin resistance suggests that different actions of insulin are involved. Insulin resistance may be characterised by specific effects on:

- *metabolism:* carbohydrate, protein, or lipid metabolism
- *growth and development:* body mass (excessive or small); lipid (amount and distribution)
- *gonadal function:* ovarian hyperandrogenism; PCOS
- *skin:* skin tags; acanthosis nigricans

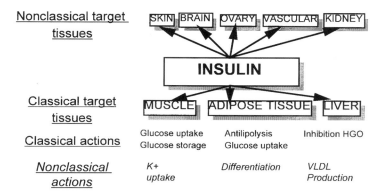

Nonclassical target tissues

SKIN BRAIN OVARY VASCULAR KIDNEY

INSULIN

Classical target tissues

MUSCLE ADIPOSE TISSUE LIVER

Classical actions

Glucose uptake	Antilipolysis	Inhibition HGO
Glucose storage	Glucose uptake	

Nonclassical actions

K+ uptake	Differentiation	VLDL Production

Figure 1 Insulin has a diverse spectrum of biological effects.

Some of the common phenotypic expressions found in patients with severe insulin resistance include muscular hypertrophy, muscle cramps, hirsutism associated with hyperandrogenism, oligomenorrhoea, alopecia, altered subcutaneous fat distribution and, in some patients, acromegaloid features.

Severe insulin resistance as a model system for hormone action

Severe insulin resistance is a useful model for studying hormone action because it shows diverse clinical phenotypes with diverse underlying molecular mechanisms that involve different chemical pathways (most of which remain undefined). In addition, affected patients provide useful material to aid understanding of the normal mechanisms of insulin action; these include receptor gene sequences, spontaneously occurring antibodies directed against epitopes on the insulin receptor, and cell lines that have enabled both genetic and acquired molecular defects to be defined.

The study of patients with severe insulin resistance permits molecular observations made *in vitro* to be applied to the development of new drugs to treat insulin resistance states. Studies in patients with severe insulin resistance have allowed physiological abnormalities to be defined and quantified *in vivo*, provided cells and tissues for *in vitro* study, and have led to the development of therapeutic approaches. Furthermore, it is likely that many of the findings from patients with severe insulin resistance can be extended to those with the much more common type 2 diabetes, in whom insulin resistance is a major feature.

Type A syndrome

Among the most common of the severe insulin resistance phenotypes, type A appears to represent a compilation of multiple molecular defects, most of which are not yet defined. Type A patients tend to present not in early childhood but as adolescents, with acanthosis nigricans and, in young women, with the signs and symptoms of hyperandrogenism noted above. Glucose tolerance levels vary between normal and overt diabetes. Autoimmune features (anti-receptor antibodies) are not present.

Many of these patients progress to intractable overt diabetes, and have severe hyperlipidaemia (often hypertriglyceridaemia) resulting in acute pancreatitis or eruptive xanthoma, together with low high density lipoprotein (HDL) levels.

It has been suggested that dyslipidaemia combined with the possible action of insulin as a growth factor on endothelial smooth muscle cells may confer an even higher risk of macrovascular disease than that sustained by patients with type 2 diabetes. Pseudoacromegaly is seen in some patients with the type A syndrome, and partial lipodystrophy may also be seen.

Natural history of the type A syndrome

An indication of the degree of insulin resistance seen in this condition is given by the results of glucose and insulin tolerance tests and decline in glycaemic control over time in the patient described by Professor O'Rahilly in the previous chapter who has an Arg1174Gln mutation. The glucose tolerance test shows massive fasting hyperinsulinaemia of over 350 (US) µU/ml (the normal level would be about 10 µU/ml), rising to 800 µU/ml during the test (Fig. 2, left). The resistance of type A patients to exogenous insulin is indicated by the minimal glucose response to a large intravenous dose of insulin in this individual, compared with that normal controls (Fig. 2, right).

Comparison of data from 1987 and 1992 in the same patient illustrates the decline in β-cell function and glycaemic control over time. Over 5 years, a normal fasting blood glucose level with mildly abnormal glucose tolerance at the expense of massive peripheral hyperinsulinaemia (2000 mU) progressed to overt diabetes, with fasting glucose of 150 mg/dl and marked but greatly reduced insulinaemia. This finding is analogous to the situation in type 2 diabetes where in the presence of moderate insulin resistance euglycaemia is maintained until some degree of β-cell dysfunction supervenes.

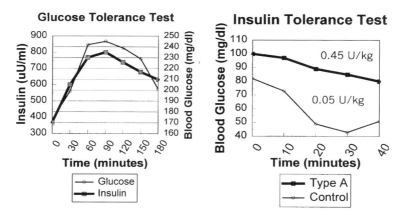

Figure 2 Type A insulin resistance syndrome; a patient with an Arg1174Gln mutation. A glucose tolerance test (left) shows massive hyperinsulinaemia, and the minimal insulin response to exogenous insulin (right) compared with that of normal controls illustrates insulin resistance.

Therapeutic approaches to insulin resistance

The study of severely insulin resistant patients in drug development

There are several advantages of studying subjects with severe insulin resistance in the drug development process. First, few or no effective treatments are available. Secondly, the mechanism of action of new agents can be studied, and thirdly, the very heterogeneity of defects and phenotypes can provide insights into the mechanisms of action of new agents. The diverse phenotypes can also be a limitation. Unfortunately, remarkably little is known about underlying molecular mechanisms, the effects of disease-modifying genes, or the natural histories of these conditions.

Potential therapeutic approaches

Possible approaches to the treatment of severe insulin resistance in general are summarised in Table 1. More promising approaches include inhibiting hepatic glucose production and sensitising (or bypassing) insulin action. Other approaches that have met with less satisfactory results include agents that delay glucose absorption, inhibit fatty acid oxidation, increase tissue blood flow (and possibly increase insulin sensitivity), block soluble mediators of insulin resistance, block counter-regulatory hormones or receptors (and so improve glycaemic control), or may activate post-receptor insulin transduction pathways (Table 1). However, none of these approaches appears to address the problem at the level of the basic molecular defect.

Table 1 Potential therapeutic approaches to treating severe insulin resistance

Therapeutic approach	Potential agents
Inhibiting hepatic glucose production	Biguanides
Sensitising insulin action	Thalizolidinediones RhIGF-I
Delaying glucose absorption	α-Glucosidase inhibitors
Inhibiting fatty acid oxidation	Etomoxir Methyl-2-tetradecylglycidate
Increasing tissue blood flow	ACE-inhibitors
Blockade of soluble mediators of insulin resistance	TNF-α blockers/inhibitors
Blockade of counter-regulatory hormones or receptors	Glucagon receptor antagonists Somatostatin agonists
Post-receptor insulin transduction pathway activators	Vanadium salts

RhIGF-I, recombinant human insulin-like growth factor-I; ACE, angiotensin converting enzyme; TNF, tissue necrosis factor.

Thalizolidinediones in the treatment of severe insulin resistance

We have conducted a double-blind, placebo-controlled crossover study of the thalizolidinedione, troglitazone, in eight patients with severe insulin resistance. After a 2-week wash-in, patients were randomized to treatment with troglitazone or placebo for 6 weeks. After a one-month wash-out they were then switched to the other treatment arm for a further 6 weeks. Tests before, between, and after the treatments assessed glycaemic control and insulin secretion over a 'modal day ' during which three meals and two snacks were consumed, or after a liquid mixed protein/carbohydrate meal. Sensitivity to exogenous insulin was measured directly using a 2–3 hour steady-state plasma glucose test (co-infusion of insulin and glucose, plus somatostatin to suppress endogenous insulin secretion).

Six patients of different phenotypes completed the study, and all tolerated the study drug well. Most showed significant improvements in serum insulin levels, in glycaemic control if they were initially hyperglycaemic, or in serum triglyceride levels if they were hypertriglyceridaemic. An example of the effects of this agent can be seen in a young woman with Dunnigan–Kobberling syndrome (hypertriglyceridaemia with lipodystrophy). During the mixed meal, blood glucose concentration was normal at baseline and after troglitazone treatment (about 80 mg/dl). However, marked insulinaemia at baseline (up to 130 mU/ml) was dramatically lowered (maximum level <70 mU/ml) after treatment (Fig. 3).

A second patient, a slim woman with type A insulin resistance, demonstrated clear fasting hyperglycaemia at baseline that increased following the mixed meal, and was associated with hyperinsulinaemia 10 times the upper limit of the normal range (Fig. 3a, left). After troglitazone therapy, although insulin levels remained high, glycaemic control improved greatly (Fig. 3a, right). Insulin sensitivity was also much improved; in steady-state plasma glucose tests after 6 weeks' troglitazone therapy, the maximum glucose level of over 320 mg/dl at baseline had fallen to about 250 mg/dl (Fig. 3b). However, a patient with complete lipoatrophy and severe hypertriglyceridaemia had no change in glycaemic control in response to troglitazone, although triglyceride levels did improve.

Insulin-like growth factor (IGF)-I

IGF is a single-chain polypeptide structurally homologous to proinsulin. There are two closely-related ligands, IGF-I and IGF-II, and a family of binding proteins (IGFBP-1 to 6). Most of the circulating IGF-I is bound to the principal binding protein IGFBP-III in a 150 kDa complex. The other binding proteins promote or inhibit the action of IGF-I or IGF-II on peripheral tissues, although their activities *in vivo* are not well understood. It appears that both IGF-I and IGF-II act primarily through the IGF-I receptor. IGF-I and insulin receptors are also structural homologues. Both are tyrosine kinase heteromeric transmembrane receptors, each binds and is activated by the other's ligands (although with lower affinity).

These receptors also have in common many intracellular signalling pathways, including the IRS (insulin response substrate) family. Both also have similar biological effects on glucose transport and sodium–hydrogen exchange. In a study in normal individuals, both insulin, 0.15 U, and

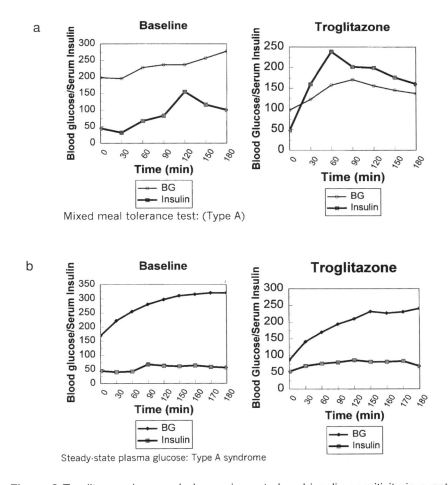

Figure 3 Troglitazone-improved glycaemic control and insulin sensitivity in a patient with type A severe insulin resistance. (a) At baseline, fasting hyperglycaemia increased by food was associated with hyperinsulinaemia 10 times the upper limit of normal (left). After 6 weeks' troglitazone therapy, glycaemic control was greatly improved (right). (b) Insulin sensitivity was also improved; steady-state plasma glucose tests after by 6 weeks' troglitazone therapy, a maximum glucose level of >320 mg/dl at baseline (left) was lowered to about 250 mg/dl (right).

recombinant human (rh) IGF-I, 100 µg/kg, caused acute hypoglycaemia (Guler *et al.* 1987).

However, many of the bioactivities of rhIGF-I and insulin *in vivo* differ in potency. At concentrations in which their glucose uptake stimulating activity is equivalent, rhIGF-I has the following inhibitory potencies relative to insulin:

- Hepatic glucose production   lower
- Protein degradation   equal
- Lipolysis   lower
- Insulin release   much greater
- Growth hormone (GH) release   much greater
- IGFBP-1 release   much lower

In contrast to IGF-I, GH induces insulin resistance and IGFBP-III production, increases insulin release, local IGF synthesis, blood glucose, and specifically decreases IGFBP-2.

rhIGF-I as a theraputic agent

As a potential therapeutic agent, IGF-I has certain disadvantages: its effects are rather pleotropic; its normal physiological role, including the precise functions of the binding proteins, is incompletely understood; and potentially unrestrained growth effects (oncogenesis or stimulation of tumour progression) give cause for concern. In addition, a large mass of injectable drug is needed, and the production costs for recombinant proteins are high. Nevertheless, research continues on the potential therapeutic role of rhIGF-I in severe insulin resistance and in other conditions in which the risk/benefit ratio is favourable.

Effects of IGF-I on patients with severe insulin resistance

It has been shown that bolus injection of IGF-I can simultaneously reduce serum insulin and glucose levels over a few hours in patients with severe insulin resistance (Schoenle *et al.* 1991). Chronic administration of rhIGF-I for more than one month reduced fasting serum glucose levels and improved glycaemic control (Kuzuya *et al.* 1993), and a two-week course of rhIGF-I gave similar results (Vestergaard *et al.* 1997).

We have studied a series of severely insulin-resistant individuals with different phenotypes, including five with type A syndrome plus diabetes, one with acquired lipodystrophy and mild type 2 diabetes, two sisters with Dunnigan–Kobberling syndrome, one with combined GHRH/LHRH deficiency and hypertriglyceridaemia, and two with acquired severe lipoatrophy. Several of these patients have been reported previously (Morrow *et al.* 1994, Moses *et al.* 1995).

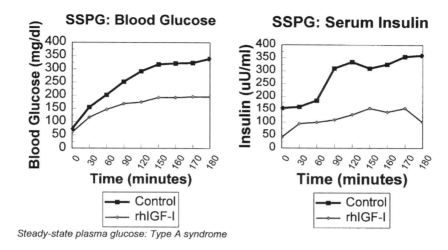

Steady-state plasma glucose: Type A syndrome

Figure 4 A steady-state serum glucose tests show that treatment with recombinant human IGF-I (rhIGF-I) greatly improved insulin sensitivity in a patient with severe insulin resistance relative to a control period; levels of serum glucose and insulin were dramatically decreased.

After baseline tests, including the steady-state plasma glucose test, these patients received rhIGF-I, 100 µg/kg twice daily for one month before retesting. We found that rhIGF-I could lower fasting insulin, fasting and 24-hour mean serum glucose levels, and mean 24-hour serum insulin levels; it could allow recovery of abnormal first-phase insulin secretion and increase insulin clearance. In addition, dramatic improvement in insulin sensitivity is illustrated by the results of the steady-state plasma glucose test in the first subject studied (Fig. 4).

Possible mechanisms of action of rhIGF-I

The mechanism of action of rhIGF-I is not well understood, and many of its observed effects are probably indirect in nature. Possible mechanisms of action include: suppression of GH, glucagon and insulin; stimulation of muscle glucose uptake and upregulation of insulin receptors (Fig. 5).

I suspect that, in the presence of insulin resistance associated with abnormalities in insulin receptor pathways, rhIGF-I in pharmacological doses alters the ratio of intercellular mediators so as to produce improvements in insulin receptor signal transduction; at the same time rhIGF-I decreases glucose toxicity, by directly lowering blood glucose concentrations and thus improving insulin sensitivity.

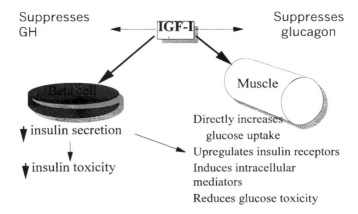

Figure 5 Possible mechanisms of action of recombinant human IGF-I (rhIGF-I) include: suppression of growth hormone, glucagon and insulin; stimulation of muscle glucose uptake, upregulation of insulin receptors and lowering of glucose toxicity.

Adverse effects of IGF-I

Adverse effects of IGF-I include: oedema of the face, periphery and optic nerve, parotid discomfort and jaw pain, tachycardia (temporally related to the presence of circulating free IGF-I), hypoglycaemia, migraine or cluster headache, Bell's palsy, pseudotumour cerebri, postural hypotension, arthralgia, testicular pain and progression of retinopathy (Jabri *et al.* 1994, RHIGF-I in NIDDM Study Group 1996).

Conclusions and the future

- Current therapeutic approaches to severe insulin resistance are generally ineffective and the following strategies should continue to be investigated: bypassing of insulin receptor/post-receptor blockade, sensitisation of insulin receptor pathways, direct stimulation of glucose transport, inhibition of hepatic gluconeogenesis, inhibition of fatty acid mobilisation or oxidation, and delay of glucose absorption.
- Despite the progress of the last 10 years, much more research is needed to unravel the many molecular defects underlying severe insulin resistance and so improve the chances of developing effective therapies.
- Such therapies will have the potential to benefit not only patients with severe insulin resistance syndromes, but also those with the much more common problems of type 2 diabetes and syndrome X (the dysmetabolic syndrome).

References

Guler HP, Zapf J & Froesch ER 1987 Short-term metabolic effects of recombinant insulin-like growth factor I in healthy adults. *New England Journal of Medicine* **317** 137–140.

Jabri N, Schalch DS, Schwartz SL *et al.* 1994 Adverse effects of recombinant insulin-like growth factor I in obese insulin-resistant type II diabetic patients. *Diabetes* **43** 369–374.

Kuzuya H, Matsuura N, Sakamoto M *et al.* 1993 Trial of insulin-like growth factor I therapy for patients with extreme insulin resistance syndromes. *Diabetes* **42** 696–705.

Morrow LA, O'Brien MB, Moller DE, Flier JS & Moses AC 1994 Recombinant human insulin-like growth factor I improves glycaemic control and insulin action in the Type A syndrome of severe insulin resistance. *Journal of Clinical Endocrinology and Metabolism* **79** 205–210.

Moses AC, Morrow LA, O'Brien MB, Moller DE & Flier JS 1995 Recombinant insulin-like growth factor I (rhIGF-I) as a therapeutic agent for hyperinsulinaemic insulin-resistant diabetes mellitus. *Diabetes Research and Clinical Practice* **28** (suppl) S185–194.

RHIGF-I in NIDDM Study Group 1996 Safety profile of rhIGF-I therapy in patients with NIDDM: a dose-ranging placebo control trial. *Diabetes* **45** (suppl) 352A.

Schoenle EJ, Zenobi PD, Torresani T, Werder EA, Zachman M & Froesch ER 1991 Recombinant insulin-like growth factor I (rhIGF-I) reduces hyperglycaemia in patients with severe insulin resistance. *Diabetologica* **34** 675–691.

Vestergaard H, Rossen M, Urhammer SA, Muller J & Pederson O 1997 Short- and long-term effects of recombinant human IGF-I in patients with severe insulin resistance and diabetes mellitus. *European Journal of Endocrinology* **136** 475–482.

What we have learnt from maturity-onset diabetes of the young

A Hattersley

School of Postgraduate Medicine and Health Sciences, University of Exeter, EX2 5AX, UK

This chapter shows how the understanding of maturity-onset diabetes of the young (MODY) has progressed from the initial clinical descriptions of the disorder in patients to investigations of the heterogeneity of the underlying genetic abnormalities. Studies of patients with genetic defects have resulted in insights into the relationships between the genotype and clinical phenotype in MODY and have advanced understanding of fetal growth.

Features of MODY

Table 1 summarises the main characteristics of MODY and the differences from those of classical non-insulin-dependent diabetes mellitus (NIDDM, type 2 diabetes). MODY is dominantly transmitted and, before insulin was discovered, when insulin dependent diabetes was invariably fatal, it was noted that a diabetic parent was a good prognostic sign for children with diabetes. After the discovery of insulin, MODY was largely unrecognised until it was rediscovered in the 1970s (Tattersall 1974, Tattersall & Fajans 1975).

Table 1 Features of NIDDM and MODY

	NIDDM	MODY
Age of onset	Middle age to old age	Adolescence to young adulthood
Genetically determined	?50%	100%
Inheritance	Polygenic/heterogeneous	Monogenic/homogeneous
Pathophysiology	β-cell/liver/muscle	β-cell

Genetic heterogeneity of MODY

There is considerable genetic heterogeneity in MODY. We have performed gene sequencing in 71 families (562 subjects) in the UK. The first mutation identified – glucokinase – appeared in 14% of families, whereas by far the most common was the hepatic nuclear factor-1α (HNF-1α) mutation, found in 44 of the 71 families (62%). These two mutations are the most important clinically.

The other genes in which mutations are only rarely found in this population are HNF-4α, HNF-1β, and insulin promoter factor-1 (IPF-1). There remain families in whom no mutations have been found (MODY x) (Beards *et al.* 1988).

Genotype-phenotype relationships in MODY

Glucokinase

Glucokinase (GCK), the pancreatic glucose sensor, is an obvious candidate gene for MODY (Matschinsky 1990). The absence of negative feedback and the low affinity for the substrate (glucose) meant it had the characteristics of a rate-determining step. Mutations were discovered throughout the GCK gene (Frogel *et al.* 1993), most of them around the glucose binding cleft, and many were found to affect glucose phosphorylation *in vitro* (Gidh-Jain *et al.* 1993).

The clear relationship between GCK mutations and a benign phenotype MODY is illustrated by the original Oxford family with a glucose mutation in whom all have mild, chronic, stable fasting hyperglycaemia managed on diet alone (Page *et al.* 1995). In contrast, patients with NIDDM show progressive deterioration in β-cell function and have increasing treatment requirements. Microvascular complications are very rare in GCK mutations.

Hepatic nuclear factor-1α

The HNF-1α gene was not an obvious candidate gene for MODY because transcription factors had not been recognised as important β-cell genes; but the work of Bell and colleagues on this gene changed our view of the β-cell (Yamagata *et al.* 1996). The transcription factor HNF-1α is regulated by HNF-4α, present in many tissues (e.g. kidney, liver, pancreas) and regulates many genes, including insulin and GCK, involved in glucose metabolism. It has a helix-turn-helix structure, and forms a functional homodimer with itself or a heterodimer with HNF-1β.

Phenotypes in patients with HNF-1α mutations are more variable than those with GCK mutations; MODY resulting from HNF-1α mutations involves progressive deterioration in blood glucose with age. Treatment varies from diet alone through oral hypoglycaemic drugs to insulin; even in a single pedigree with the same HNF-1α mutation. Microvascular complications are frequent (Hattersley 1998).

Further specific features of families with a HNF-1α defect include a low renal glucose threshold(Menzel *et al.* 1997), as first described by Tattersall (1974) and sensitivity to sulphonylureas when first treated. For example, we found that a fasting serum glucose level of 10 mmol/l in one individual was reduced by 2.5 mg glibenclamide to 2 mmol/l, 4 hours post-dose. This suggests that the β-cell defect resulting an HNF-1α mutation occurs within the beta cell before the sulphonylurea receptor.

The mutation mechanisms in HNF-1α defects are uncertain. It appears that mutations that operate in a dominant negative fashion may have a more severe phenotype than those with a simple gene-dosage effect (Hattersley *et al.* unpublished data). Diabetes is found only in the homozygous, not the heterozygous, knockout mouse. In addition, recent studies on an artificial severe dominant negative HNF-1α defect in an insulinoma cell line showed that it decreased not only gene transcription of insulin, glucose transporter 2 and pyruvate kinase, but also glucose utilisation and mitochondrial oxidation. The progressive nature of β-cell dysfunction may suggest not just a simple altered transcription of metabolic enzymes, but also a possible developmental impairment in the fetal pancreas.

Differences in β-cell function

Individuals with an HNF-1α mutation are born with essentially normal β-cell function which deteriorates over time, whereas those with a GCK mutation initially have half the normal β-cell function, which deteriorates only slightly with age (Hattersley 1998). The insulin secretion rate curve in response to glucose is right-shifted in GCK patients relative to unaffected controls, so that a normal serum insulin level results in a serum glucose level of 5 mmol/l in an unaffected person, but about 7.5 mmol/l in a GCK patient (Byrne *et al.* 1994). Non-diabetic patients with an HNF-1α mutation maintain normal insulin secretion at normal fasting glucose levels, but do not increase it in response to an oral glucose load and become markedly hyperglycaemic (Byrne *et al.* 1996). In addition, serum glucose level is strongly related to body mass index (BMI) in patients with the HNF-1α mutation but unrelated in those with the GCK glucose-sensing defect. Thus, patients with these mutations can now be distinguished on clinical criteria (Table 2).

Table 2 Comparison of clinical features of MODY in patients with a glucokinase (GCK) or HNF-1α defect

GCK		HNF-1α
At birth	FPG elevated	Normal glucose tolerance
Deterioration with age	Very slow	Progressive after diabetes develops
Symptoms	Rare	Common
Relationship to BMI	Unrelated	Strong relationship
Increment during OGTT*	Small (<3.5 mmol/l)	Large (>5 mmol/l)

FPG, Fasting plasma glucose.
*The difference between fasting and 2-hour value.

Insulin promoter factor-1

Can the study of the rare defects of MODY provide insights into normal development and physiology? The insulin gene transcription factor IPF-1 (also known as PDX) is one example of this. Elegant work in rodents has shown that transcription factors are expressed in developing pancreatic cells during their differentiation from endodermal to mature pancreatic cells secreting exocrine products, somatostatin, insulin, pancreatic polypeptide (PP) or glucagon. IPF-1, at various concentrations, plays a key role at different stages of the differentiation process (Edlund 1998). In the mature islets, IPF-1 is also the crucial transcription factor regulating expression of the insulin gene.

These findings translate to humans. In one family, a single child with pancreatic agenesis was shown to be homozygous for a frameshift mutation in IPF-1(Stoffers *et al.* 1997a). Heterozygous mutation carriers had early onset diabetes with autosomal dominant inheritance and had MODY (Stoffers *et al.* 1997b).

In studies on IPF-1 defects in our UK patients, we have found three mutations (C18R, D76N, R197H) in 48 patients with early-onset NIDDM. All the mutations caused reduced insulin transcription *in vitro* and predispose to NIDDM in case/control and familial association studies. As with the HNF-1α mentioned above, a key question yet to be clarified is whether IFP1 defects lead to β-cell dysfunction by altering gene transcription, or by affecting pancreatic differentiation and development.

So the clinical phenotype of the affected individual depends on how severe the IPF-1 mutation is and whether it is inherited in heterozygous or homozygous fashion:

- Homozygous severe: pancreatic agenesis
- Heterozygous severe: MODY
- Heterozygous moderate: monogenic NIDDM
- Heterozygous mild: predisposition to NIDDM.

Hepatic nuclear factor-1β

The study of the very uncommon mutation of the transcription factor HNF-1β showed that it was associated with the development of MODY and renal disease including chronic renal failure, cystic kidneys and proteinuria (Horikawa *et al.* 1997). We found a 4 bp deletion (CCTC) in exon four, resulting in a frame shift mutation. Thus a 'renal phenotype' is co-inherited with the mutation in HNF-1β that is responsible for the β-cell defect leading to MODY. Histological evidence suggests that HNF-1β is crucial for early fetal nephron development.

Fetal development, birth weight and diabetes

A striking inverse association seems exists between weight at birth and relative risk of the development of impaired glucose tolerance or NIDDM in later life (Hales *et al.* 1991). The mechanism for this is not understood.

Is there a genetic explanation for the association of low birth weight with diabetes in later life?

The thrifty phenotype hypothesis was proposed to explain these findings: low birthweight results from intra-uterine malnutrition, and the compensatory insulin resistance becomes disadvantageous in adulthood when food intake is plentiful resulting in an increased risk of NIDDM, hypertension and ischaemic heart disease.

The current clinical treatment of diabetes in pregnancy and the avoidance of macrosomia in the newborn are based on Pederson's 1977 monograph. This proposed that the sensing of elevated maternal serum glucose by the fetal pancreas leads to increased fetal insulin secretion, increased insulin-mediated growth and a large hyperglycaemic neonate (Pederson 1977).

We hypothesized that a defect in the GCK gene would lead to reduced glucose sensing by the fetal pancreas, leading to lower birthweight. This hypothesis was tested in 21 sibling pairs, one member of which had a GCK mutation and the other was unaffected. In 19/21 pairs, birthweight was much lower in the affected than in the unaffected sibling, and the 0.5 kg mean difference between the two groups was highly significant ($P = 0.0003$ paired Student's *t*-test) (Hattersley *et al.* 1998) (Fig. 1).

The interrelationship between the fetal and maternal phenotype, and birthweight was particularly interesting. Birthweight was greatest (86th centile) when the mother was hyperglycaemic and had the mutation, but the fetus was not affected. Conversely, the baby was small at birth (25th centile) when the mother was unaffected but the fetus had inherited the defect from the father. The difference was highly significant (ANOVA $P < 0.001$). Presence of the mutation in both mother and fetus effectively cancelled out any effect on birthweight (Hattersley *et al.* 1998).

The fetal insulin hypothesis

These results led us to the fetal insulin hypothesis: fetal genetics that affected fetal glucose sensing, fetal insulin secretion and insulin resistance

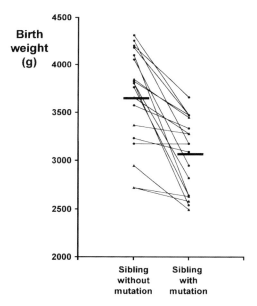

Figure 1 Birth weight according to glucokinase mutation status. Among 21 sibling pairs, mean birthweight was significantly lower in the siblings with GCK gene defects causing impaired glucose sensing than in unaffected siblings; mean difference was 0.5 kg ($P = 0.0003$). (Reproduced from Hattersley *et al.* 1998 with permission.)

would alter insulin-mediated growth and hence birthweight. This hypothesis is supported by available data on the effects of monogenic subtypes on fetal growth (Table 3). However, this information on rare genetic syndromes does not apply to the general population and cannot explain the general association between birthweight and subsequent NIDDM risk. It does establish the principle that genetic defects altering fetal insulin secretion or fetal insulin resistance would alter birthweight.

Table 3 Testing the fetal insulin hypothesis using monogenic subtypes (Hattersley *et al.* 1998)

Syndrome	Gene	Fetal growth
Glucose sensing		
Glucokinase	GCK	Decreased
Insulin secretion		
Pancreatic agenesis	IFP1	Greatly decreased
Neonatal diabetes	pat 6q22	Greatly decreased
Nesidioblastosis	SUR/Kir6.2	Greatly increased
Insulin action		
Donahue's syndrome*	Insulin receptor	Greatly decreased

*'Leprechaunism'.

Consequently, we propose that an insulin resistant genotype may lower the response to fetal insulin *in utero*, resulting in low birth weight as well as insulin resistance in childhood and adult life and so predispose the individual to NIDDM, hypertension, and ischaemic heart disease. Thus, these common conditions may after all have a genetic basis.

Conclusions

- MODY is a β-cell disorder, the major causes of which are defects in the glycolytic enzyme GCK or the transcription factor HNF-1α.
- The genotypes result in very different phenotypes.
- Patients with the glucose-sensing GCK defect have mild, stable, asymptomatic, hyperglycaemia from birth, do not need pharmacological treatment and rarely have microvascular complications.
- Diabetes associated with the non-glucose-sensing HNF-1α defect usually appears at adolescence or early adulthood and becomes progressively severe requiring insulin or tablets in most patients and resulting in microvascular complications.

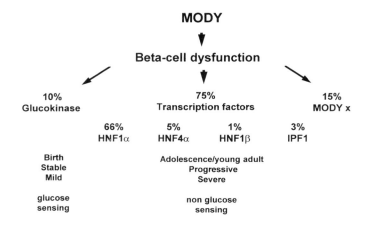

Figure 2 The genetic basis and clinical features of MODY subtypes. Data from Hattersley 1998.

- Studies on these defects have provided insights into normal fetal development.
- Figure 2 presents an overview.

We are grateful to the members of more than 250 families referred to us by their physicians from across the UK who made our research possible.

References

Beards F, Frayling T, Bulman M *et al.* 1988 Mutations in hepatocyte nuclear factor 1 beta are not a common cause of maturity-onset diabetes of the young in the UK. *Diabetes* **47** 1152–1154.

Byrne MM, Sturis J, Clement K *et al.* 1994 Insulin secretory abnormalities in subjects with hyperglycemia due to glucokinase mutations. *Journal of Clinical Investigation* **93** 1120–1130.

Byrne MM, Sturis J, Menzel S *et al.* 1996 Altered insulin secretory responses to glucose in diabetic and nondiabetic subjects with mutations in the diabetes susceptibility gene MODY3 on Chromosome 12. *Diabetes* **45** 1503–1510.

Edlund H 1998 Transcribing pancreas. *Diabetes* **47** 1817–1823.

Froguel P, Zouali H, Vionnet N *et al.* 1993 Familial hyperglycemia due to mutations in glucokinase. Definition of a subtype of diabetes mellitus. *New England Journal of Medicine* **328** 697–702.

Gidh-Jain M, Takeda J, Xu LZ *et al.* 1993 Glucokinase mutations associated with non-insulin-dependent (type 2) diabetes mellitus have decreased enzymatic activity: implications for structure/function relationships. *Proceedings of the National Academy of Sciences of the United States of America* **90** 1932–1936.

Hales CN, Barker DJP, Clark PMS *et al.* 1991 Fetal and infant growth and impaired glucose tolerance at age 64. *British Medical Journal* **303** 1019–1022.

Hattersley AT, Beards F, Ballantyne E, Appleton M, Harvey R & Ellard S 1998 Mutations in the glucokinase gene of the fetus result in reduced birth weight. *Nature Genetics* **19** 268–270.

Hattersley AT 1998 Maturity-onset diabetes of the young: clinical heterogeneity explained by genetic heterogeneity. *Diabetic Medicine* **15** 15–24.

Horikawa Y, Iwasaki N, Hara M *et al.* 1997 Mutation in hepatocyte nuclear factor-1b gene (TCF2) associated with MODY. *Nature Genetics* **17** 384–385.

Matschinsky FM 1990 Glucokinase as glucose sensor and metabolic signal generator in pancreatic β-cell and hepatocytes. *Diabetes* **30** 647–752.

Menzel S, Kaisaki P, Menzel R *et al.* 1997 Phenotype of human hepatocyte nuclear factor 1α mutations: diabetes late complications, and glucosuria. *Diabetologia* **40** A161.

Page RC, Hattersley AT, Levy JC *et al.* 1995 Clinical characteristics of subjects with a missense mutation in glucokinase. *Diabetic Medicine* **12** 209–217.

Pederson J 1977 *The Pregnant Diabetic and Her New Born: Problems and Management*, pp. 211–220. Baltimore: Williams & Wilkins.

Stoffers DA, Ferrer J, Clarke WL & Habener JF 1997 Early-onset type-II diabetes mellitus (MODY4) linked to IPF1. *Nature Genetics* **17** 138–139.

Stoffers DA, Zinkin NT, Stanojevic V, Clarke WL & Habener JF 1997 Pancreatic agenesis attributable to a single nucleotide deletion in the human IPF1 gene coding sequence. *Nature Genetics* **15** 106–110.

Tattersall RB & Fajans SS 1975 A difference between the inheritance of classical juvenile-onset and maturity-onset type diabetes of young people. *Diabetes* **24** 44–53.

Tattersall RB 1974 Mild familial diabetes with dominant inheritance. *Quarterly Journal of Medicine* **43** 339–357.

Yamagata K, Oda N, Kaisaki PJ *et al.* 1996 Mutations in the hepatic nuclear factor 1 alpha gene in maturity-onset diabetes of the young (MODY3). *Nature* **384** 455–458.

Genetic Insights in Paediatric Endocrinology and Metabolism
Eds S O'Rahilly and D B Dunger
BioScientifica Ltd, Bristol (1999)

The genetics and causes of type 1 diabetes

J Todd

Cambridge Institute for Medical Research, Addenbrookes Hospital,
Hills Road, Cambridge CB2 2XY, UK

Type 1 diabetes is an autoimmune disorder in which at least two common genetic variants, affecting the major histocompatability complex (MHC) human leucocyte antigen (HLA) class II proteins and the insulin gene promoter, interact with environmental factors. Analysis of how these function and interact is leading to an emerging picture of the basic causes of type 1 diabetes. Common gene variants such as these are more difficult to track down than uncommon ones, but it is important that this be done because they have a very great impact on phenotypes and the number of cases in the population. This topic has been reviewed recently (Todd 1999).

Insulin-dependent diabetes

The major cause of type 1, insulin-dependent diabetes mellitus (IDDM) is an autoimmunity against the insulin-producing β-cells of the pancreatic islets. In Fig. 1 the β-cells (in the centre) are surrounded by T-lymphocytes, along with macrophages and dendritic cells, which invade the pancreas and islets, and irreversibly destroy the β-cells.

Genetic analysis during the last 10 years has provided significant insights into the causes of the T-cell-mediated inflammation and autoimmune β-cell destruction.

Pathology of type 1 diabetes

The major step in the pathogenesis of type 1 diabetes is the interaction between the T-lymphocyte and an 'antigen-presenting cell' (e.g. B-lymphocyte, macrophage, dendritic cell) (Fig. 2). Unlike B-lymphocytes, which can directly recognise antigens, T-lymphocytes can recognise antigens only after they have been processed by proteases within the antigen-presenting cells. These cells break down the foreign (or self) antigenic protein into peptides that are transported onto the surface of the presenting

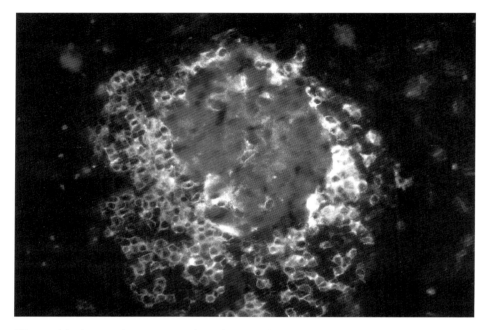

Figure 1 In the autoimmune reaction of type 1 diabetes, the pancreatic β-cells (centre) are surrounded and eventually destroyed by invading T-lymphocytes (outside), macrophages and dendritic cells.

cell by HLA/MHC-Ag class II binding receptor molecules; only then can they be recognised by the CD4 T-lymphocyte antigen receptor (TCR) (Cucca & Todd 1996).

Genetic variation in the peptide-binding site of the class II molecule accounts for about 50% of the familial clustering of the disease. Two main class II alleles that predispose to diabetes are designated DR3 and DR4.

The MHC class II molecule is highly polymorphic in the normal population. The many forms all bind different peptides, leading to wide variations in the efficacy of the individual immune response to a pathogen or other antigen challenge. The same variation predisposes some individuals to autoimmune responses directly through peptide binding.

Alleles predisposing for type 1 diabetes

A major question in the pathogenesis of type 1 diabetes is: which of the many possible β-cell proteins is the key target of the immune response in individuals who carry the diabetes susceptibility class II allele? Is there only one protein, or are several proteins involved? The most important

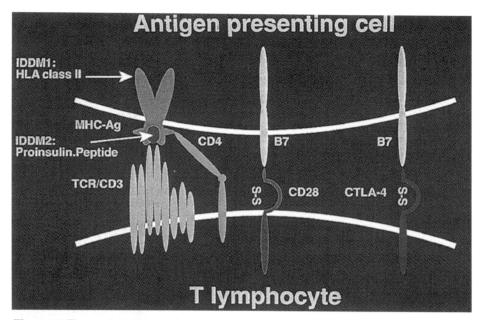

Figure 2 The major step in the pathogenesis of type 1 diabetes is the interaction between the T-lymphocyte and an antigen-presenting cell (e.g. B-lymphocyte, macrophage, dendritic cell).

susceptibility gene, designated *IDDM1* (Fig. 2), affects the MHC class II molecules, but there is good evidence for the involvement of a second gene, *IDDM2* (Fig. 2), which is a common promoter polymorphism in the insulin gene itself.

The promoter polymorphism that affects type 1 diabetes in the insulin gene has two main alleles; the predisposing genotype at the insulin polymorphism occurs in about 50% of European-derived populations. Using genetic analysis of the promoter polymorphism in insulin, we began to gain insights into the mechanism and identity of one of the key autoantigens in type 1 diabetes – pre-proinsulin itself.

The class II molecule consists of an α- and a β-chain; bound within the cleft are peptides resulting from the breakdown of self and foreign proteins. Some years ago we found that polymorphism within the binding site determines susceptibility and resistance to diabetes (Todd *et al.* 1987). More recent work has shown that an aspartic acid in the β-chain (residue 57) can form a salt bridge with the α–chain. This pairing of α- and β-chains has a profound effect on the peptide-binding capacity of the molecule and also correlates well with diabetes resistance (Nepom *et al.* 1996). One such allele encodes for aspartic acid at position 57 is DR2. Even one copy of this allele confers an almost complete lifelong protection against the disorder, in a manner as yet unexplained.

Recently, in the spontaneous mouse model of autoimmune β-cell destruction, it has been shown that a component of the resistance encoded by the salt-bridged subtype of MHC class II molecules probably arises from one of the central functions of these molecules, namely the apoptotic destruction of autoimmune T-lymphocytes within the thymus where they are produced (Todd 1999).

The HLA class II (and class I) molecules are among the most polymorphic proteins in the human body, a feature that has evidently been preserved through natural selection by infectious disease because of the survival benefits it confers. Residue 57 must be particularly valuable for resistance to infection. It is present in most mammalian species so far analysed, and some class II molecules differing by this residue alone are maintained in human populations at very high frequency. Thus this residue, perhaps through its unique role in salt-bridging the chains together, has been under great selection pressure, and plays a pivotal role in resistance and susceptibility to the autoimmune disease known as type 1 diabetes.

Promoter polymorphism in the insulin gene

As already noted, the second gene implicated in resistance and susceptibility is an insertion/deletion promoter *(INS* VNTR) polymorphism in the insulin gene itself. The two main alleles are class I and class III. It was shown that two 'short' class I alleles (+/+, Table 1) confer a greater than 3-fold relative risk of developing type 1 diabetes. However, the class III allele (–) is dominantly protective, both heterozygotes and homozygotes having a relative risk of less than 0.5 (Table 1) (Bennett *et al.* 1995).

Thus type 1 diabetes is not caused by a recessive trait at *INS* VNTR, but is explained by a dominant gain-of-function trait, suggesting that insulin

Table 1 The INS VNTR class III allele (–) is dominantly protective against diabetes

Genotype	RR	95% CI	P value
+/+	3.5	2.1–5.9	2×10^{-5}
+/–	0.3	0.2–0.6	6×10^{-4}
–/–	0.4	0.2–0.8	0.009

RR, Relative risk; CI, confidence interval.

expression might occur in the thymus, and be affected by the promoter polymorphism. Consistent with this hypothesis, we found that in the thymus the VNTR class III allele promoted insulin gene expression (mRNA) 2–3 times greater than that promoted by the VNTR class I allele, and that the reverse was true in the pancreas (Vafiadis *et al.* 1997). It seems that class III protects against type 1 diabetes by elevating pre-proinsulin, proinsulin, or insulin itself in the thymus, creating a higher level of T-lymphocyte tolerance to these key autoantigens. This agrees with a large body of evidence from animal studies (Todd 1999).

There is a degree of coincidence between the two susceptibility genes *IDDM1*, (MHC class II molecules) and IDDM2 (insulin promoter polymorphism). Recent histological studies on human thymus reveal that some medullary epithelial cells co-express both diabetes genes, and it may be that this co-expression underlies the mechanism of the combined action of *IDDM1* and *IDDM2* (Todd & Willcox, unpublished observations). However, it is clear from human and mouse studies that the presence of the two susceptibility genes is not alone enough to cause type 1 diabetes. The recognition and presentation of autoantigens shown in Fig. 2 represents only one step of the disease, but other genes are needed to cause progression to T-lymphocyte-mediated inflammation and autoimmunity (Todd 1999); a permissive environment is also needed. Access to the Human Genome Project final results will greatly facilitate fine mapping of these genes by providing a full DNA sequence of the genome, identity and location of all genes and their allelic variants.

Selective increase of disease in urbanised populations

The human genome has evolved over millions of years in response to active outdoor life with a hunter–gatherer diet (e.g. roots and insects), and has developed the capacity to survive long periods of starvation and infectious disease. The advantage of polymorphisms in the HLA system – in which there are hundreds of different alleles of MHC HLA molecules – and in other systems are that a wide range of immune responses existed in the population, so that the species as a whole could survive when it encountered a fatal infectious disease.

The genome, now placed in a clean urbanised environment, with effective healthcare and a very different diet is giving rise to increases in 'diseases of civilisation': hypertension, obesity, type 2 diabetes, cardiovascular disease, asthma and autoimmune disorders (Todd 1991, Ong *et al.* 1999). Common themes running through this list are insulin resistance and T-cell mediated inflammation, with a hyperactive polymorphic immune response. This agrees with results from animal studies in which an infectious environment effectively protected mice from developing type 1 diabetes.

A third gene in type I diabetes

Evidence is accumulating that one of the major pathways affecting autoimmune disease is the cytokine interleukin-2 (IL-2). The IL-2 knockout mouse develops fatal autoimmune disease that can be prevented by treatment with IL-2, showing that IL-2 is essential for immunological self-tolerance; it terminates T-lymphocyte action by stimulating apoptosis. From genetic analysis in animals and indirect evidence in humans we have shown that susceptibility to type 1 diabetes maps directly to structural polymorphism in the IL-2 gene (Denny *et al.* 1997). We believe that this is the third diabetes gene predisposing to autoimmunity, and may regulate T-lymphocyte-mediated inflammation (Todd 1999).

Conclusions and the future

- The causes of type 1 diabetes include immune recognition of β-cell protein, modulated by MHC class II genes operating in the thymus, and the effects of other genes (e.g. IL-2) on the immune system. It is possible that some genes yet to be discovered are active in the β-cell, and their products protect the cell from immune attack.
- When available, the complete human genome map should help identification of genetic variants responsible for most features of type 1 diabetes and will provide some new insights into the basic mechanisms of the disease.
- Therapy for this disease will ultimately be rationalised by genotype; genotyping will allow identification of causative inherited biochemical mechanisms, providing surrogate markers and biochemical assays that can be used for testing the therapeutic potential of agents known to affect the pathways involved.

References

Bennett ST, Lucassen AM, Gough SCL, Powell EE, Undlien DE, Pritchard LE, Merriman ME *et al.* 1995 Susceptibility to human type 1 diabetes at *IDDM2* is determined by tandem repeat variation at the insulin gene minisatellite locus. *Nature Genetics* **9** 284–292.

Cucca F & Todd JA 1996 HLA susceptibility to type 1 diabetes: methods and mechanisms. In HLA/MHC: Genes, Molecules and Function, pp 383–406. Eds MJ Browning & AJ McMichael. Oxford: Bios Scientific Publishers.

Denny P, Lord CJ, Hill NJ, Goy JV, Levy ER, Podolin PL, Peterson LB *et al.* 1997 Mapping of the insulin-dependent diabetes locus, *Idd3*, to a 0.35 cM interval containing the *Interleukin-2* gene. *Diabetes* **46** 695–700.

Nepom BS, Nepom GT, Coleman M & Kwok WW 1996 Critical contribution of b chain residue 57 in peptide binding ability of both HLA-DR and -DQ molecules. *Proceedings of the National Academy of Sciences of the USA* **93** 7202–7206.

Ong KKL, Phillips DI, Fall C, Poulton J, Bennett ST, Golding J, Todd JA *et al.* 1999 The insulin gene VNTR, type 2 diabetes and birth weight. *Nature Genetics* **21** 262–263.

Todd JA, Bell JI & McDevitt HO 1987 HLA-DQb gene contributes to susceptibility and resistance to insulin-dependent diabetes mellitus. *Nature* **329** 599–604.

Todd JA 1991 A protective role of the environment in the development of type 1 diabetes? *Diabetic Medicine* **8** 906–910.

Todd JA 1999 From genomics to aetiology in a multifactorial disease, type 1 diabetes. *Bioessays* **21** 164–174.

Vafiadis P, Bennett ST, Todd JA, Nadeau J, Grabs R, Goodyer CG, Wickramasinghe S *et al.* 1997 Insulin expression in human thymus is modulated by INS VNTR alleles at the *IDDM2* locus. *Nature Genetics* **15** 289–292.

Genetic Insights in Paediatric Endocrinology and Metabolism
Eds S O'Rahilly and D B Dunger
BioScientifica Ltd, Bristol (1999)

Aspects of G-protein signalling in health and disease

A M Spiegel

National Institute of Diabetes and Digestive and Kidney Diseases, National Institutes of Health, Bethesda MD 20817, USA

Heterotrimeric G-proteins play a key role in coupling light and olfactory receptors – in addition to the receptors for many hormones and neurotransmitters – to such cellular effectors as ion channels and enzymes of second messenger metabolism. Martin Rodbell at the US National Institutes of Health shared the Nobel Prize for the discovery of the G-proteins in 1994, in elucidating the mechanism of action of glucagon in the hepatocyte membrane. Sequence variation in components of the G-protein-coupled signal transduction pathway is an important contributor to human disease

An overview of the continuing understanding of G-protein-coupled signal transduction and regulation is presented here, with examples of both loss- and gain-of-function mutations of G-protein α-subunits, particularly the ubiquitously expressed G_S-α protein, which is involved in the generation of cAMP through coupling to the effector adenylyl cyclase; these disorders are striking examples of dysfunctions in a particular α-subunit. Examples are discussed of how such mutations in a G-protein-coupled receptor (GPCR) lead to disease, focusing on one member of the GPCR, the calcium-sensing receptor.

G-protein-coupled signal transduction

The elements needed for G-protein-coupled signal transduction are shown in Fig. 1. The three elements originally thought to be sufficient are:
- transmembrane receptors
- G-proteins
- effectors.

Transmembrane receptors are activated by agonists of many kinds (e.g. adrenergic, muscarinic, dopaminergic). A key question yet to be answered is that of exactly how agonist binding causes the conformational change in a GPCR that allows interaction with and activation of the G-protein – the essential first step in signal transduction. The number of known GPCRs runs

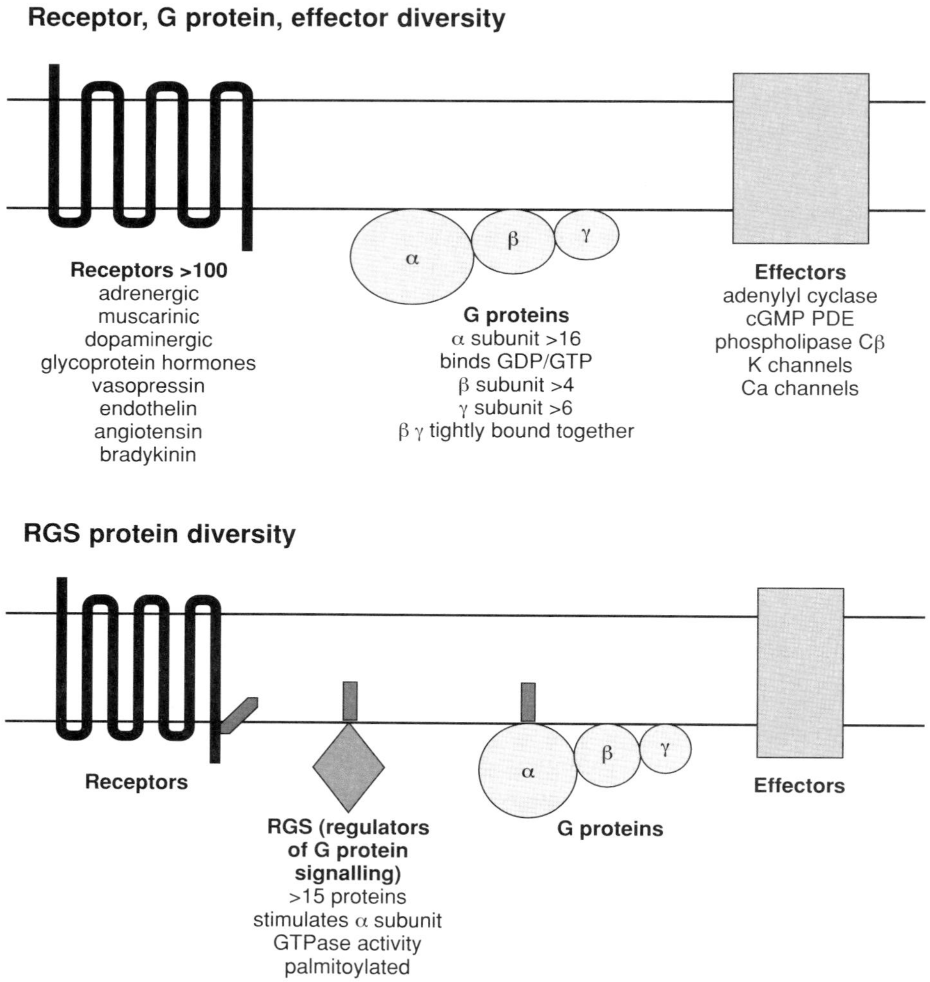

Receptor, G protein, effector diversity

Receptors >100	G proteins	Effectors
adrenergic		adenylyl cyclase
muscarinic	α subunit >16	cGMP PDE
dopaminergic	binds GDP/GTP	phospholipase Cβ
glycoprotein hormones	β subunit >4	K channels
vasopressin	γ subunit >6	Ca channels
endothelin	β γ tightly bound together	
angiotensin		
bradykinin		

RGS protein diversity

Receptors	RGS (regulators of G protein signalling)	G proteins	Effectors
	>15 proteins		
	stimulates α subunit		
	GTPase activity		
	palmitoylated		

Figure 1 The four elements needed for G-protein-coupled signal transduction.

into hundreds (genes for odorant receptors alone occupying a significant proportion – perhaps 10% – of the human genome) (Buck & Axel 1991).

G-proteins are attached to the inner surface of the cell membrane. They are heterotrimeric. The α-subunit binds the guanine nucleotide, at least 16 α-subunits exist in humans and other mammals, and their range of expression varies widely, from localised primary sensory transducers to ubiquitous cAMP production; G-protein mutations differ in their phenotypic consequences according to their range of distribution. The β- and γ-subunits form a tightly linked heterodimer.

Effectors include ion channels, adenylyl cyclase (leading to cAMP production), and many others.

Regulators of G-protein signalling (RGSs)

Recently, a fourth essential element of G-protein-coupled signal transduction – the family of RGS proteins – has been identified independently by several research groups (Dohlman & Thorner 1997), and has introduced a new dimension into the understanding of the G-protein signalling pathway. At least 15 RGSs are found in mammals. They can interact with the G-protein α-subunit and stimulate its GTPase activity, and some subtypes interact with the β-subunit *via* a γ-like domain, opening up the possibility of novel functions. Furthermore, some RGS proteins not only regulate G-proteins, but also are themselves effectors (e.g. the p115Rho guanine nucleotide exchange factor) (Kozasa *et al.* 1998).

GTPase cycle

The GTPase cycle (Fig. 2) is a characteristic of all GTP-binding-proteins. All such binding-proteins act as conformational switches that change shape as a function of GDP *vs* GTP binding. The G-protein α-subunit tightly binds GDP (Fig. 2(1)) until an agonist activates the transmembrane receptor (Fig. 2(2)); this causes the receptor to activate the G-protein, dissociating it from GDP, allowing GTP to bind in its place, and leading to dissociation of the α- and β/γ-subunits (Fig. 2(3)). Either or both of these subunits can then modulate the activity of effectors, resulting in downstream signal transduction (Fig. 2(4)). The α-subunit also acts as a timer switch; its intrinsic GTPase activity halts cycle activation by hydrolysing the γ-phosphate and returning the GTP to GDP, whereupon the α- and β/γ-subunits reassociate (Fig. 2(5)). This GTPase activity is also stimulated by RGS proteins.

Genetic defects of G-protein signalling

Mutations in the genes for both G-proteins and the GPCR have been identified as the cause of a variety of human diseases, examples of which are reviewed below. In endocrine disorders, loss-of-function mutations result in phenotypes that mimic hormone deficiencies, even though the agonist is

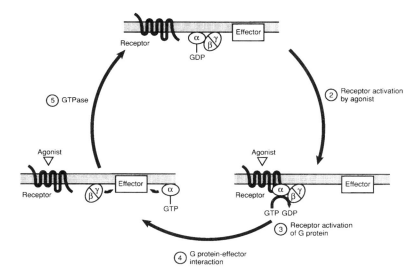

Figure 2 The GTPase cycle of G-protein-coupled signal transduction. Further explanation is in the text.

usually overabundant. On the other hand, some mutations result in gain of function, and these can provide insights into the basic mechanism of receptor activation. Receptors are always in equilibrium between activated (interacting with G-protein) and inactive conformation. The equilibrium is normally shifted towards the silent configuration, and agonist binding promotes activation; but some naturally occurring mutations give rise to the active receptor configuration in the absence of agonist. So they cause disease and also suggest which key residues might be involved in normal receptor activation. *Activating* mutations in the α-subunit cause *loss* of GTPase activity, so that it remains in its GTP-bound constitutively activated state and continues downstream signalling.

McCune–Albright syndrome (MAS)

The eponymous authors independently described the complex phenotype of this disorder; it is caused by a somatic mutation affecting the ubiquitously expressed G-protein Gs-α, that couples many hormone receptors to the stimulation of cAMP formation (Table 1).

The gain-of-function mutation responsible for MAS occurs sporadically and leads to multiple phenotypic features, notably agonist-independent endocrine overactivity resulting in precocious puberty, acromegaly,

Table 1 Features of the McCune-Albright syndrome (Weinstein *et al.* 1991)

Mutation
somatic, not germline

Phenotype
pleiotropic: fibrous dysplasia, café-au-lait skin pigmentation, autonomous
endocrine hyperfunction (gonads, somatotroph, adrenal cortex, thyroid)

cAMP
as stimulator of endocrine and melanocyte growth and function

Somatic mutation of Gs-α (R201)
reduced GTPase, constitutive cAMP formation; germline lethal?

Phenotype dependent on timing of somatic mutation
early, severe and widespread; late, focal

hypercortisolism and hyperthyroidism. The hypothesis that overproduction of cAMP due to a somatic mutation was responsible for stimulating endocrine and melanocyte activity has been confirmed. It is believed that constitutive formation of cAMP in every cell due to an early mutation would be lethal, and that later timing of the somatic mutation results in a milder and more focal phenotype (Weinstein *et al.* 1991).

Pseudohypoparathyroidism (PHP)

PHP was the first hormone-resistance disorder to be described (Albright *et al.* 1942). It is caused by a loss-of-function mutation and shows the classic phenotype of hypoparathyroidism (hypocalcaemia and hyperphosphataemia in the absence of renal failure). However, PHP is due not to deficiency of parathyroid hormone (PTH), but resistance to it. Some PHP patients show features of Albright hereditary osteodystrophy (AHO), including short stature, round face and mild mental retardation. (Other genetically distinct cases of PHP lack AHO-like features). The genetic defect in this disorder is proximal to cAMP (Chase *et al.* 1969); we and colleagues elsewhere found that a 50% deficiency in Gs-α invariably occurred in the blood cells and other peripherally available cells of individuals with combined AHO and PHP (Levine *et al.* 1980).

The 13-exon Gs-α gene was mapped to the distal long arm of chromosome 20, and numerous heterozygously transmitted loss-of-function mutations have been detected in this gene. Mutations of residues at the

C-terminus which are involved in receptor interactions may result in uncoupling of the G-protein from the receptor. Some individuals with PHP have an A366S mutation, and yet other mutations lead to loss of β/γ interaction, or guanine nucleotide binding functions.

The question arises, however: if a germline Gs-α mutation results in a 50% deficit of Gs in peripheral cells, why should hormone resistance occur with some Gs-coupled receptors (e.g. PTH, TSH) and not others (ADH, ACTH)? Patients with so-called pseudopseudohypoparathyroidism (PPHP) are first-degree relatives of PHP patients with subtle manifestations of AHO; they have the same mutation but show no hormone resistance (Weinstein 1998).

Imprinting in PHP

It now appears that maternal transmission of the Gs-α mutation results in full-blown PHP with hormone resistance, whereas if the father passes on the disease gene the offspring have PPHP. These findings are explained in terms of non-Mendelian imprinting of the Gs-α gene; a mutation in the maternal gene is expressed, leading to PHP, but a paternal mutation is suppressed by imprinting and PPHP is seen (Davies & Hughes 1993). Studies on the Gs-α knockout mouse have elucidated this. Imprinting – and hence expression or non-expression of Gs-α with consequent hormone resistance – can even be specific to individual tissues and regions; it has been found in the renal cortex and in white and brown adipose tissue. Naturally, homozygous forms – expressing no G-protein – are lethal (Yu *et al.* 1998).

Loss-of-function mutations in GPCRs

Table 2 lists disorders caused by GPCR loss-of-function mutations, most of which are autosomal and recessively inherited. Studies on visual transduction yielded the first reports of such receptor defects, but of particular interest are two disorders caused by mutations of the calcium-sensing receptor (CaR): familial hypocalciuric hypercalcaemia and neonatal severe primary hyperparathyroidism

Familial hypocalciuric hypercalcaemia (FHH) and neonatal severe primary hyperparathyroidism (NSPH)

FHH, a disorder of calcium sensing manifested in the parathyroid and kidney, is autosomal dominant with complete penetrance, and is present from birth (Brown *et al.* 1998). NSPH is genetically related to FHH. The

Table 2 Disorders caused by GPCR loss-of-function mutations (Spiegel 1998)

Receptor	Disorder	Inheritance
Cone opsins	colour blindness	R,X
Rhodopsin	retinitis pigmentosa	D,R
V2 vasopressin	nephrogenic diabetes insipidus	X
ACTH	familial ACTH resistance	R
LH	male pseudohermaphroditism	R
TSH	familial hypothyroidism	R
CaR	*familial hypocalciuric hypercalcaemia/*	*D*
	neonatal severe primary hyperparathyroidism	*R*
Thromboxane A2	congenital bleeding	R
Endothelin B	Hirschsprung disease	R
FSH	hypergonadotropic ovarian failure	R
TRH	central hyperthyroidism	R
GHRH	GH deficiency	R
GNRH	hypogonadotropic hypogonadism	R
PTH	Blomstrand chondrodysplasia	R

D, autosomal dominant; R, autosomal recessive; X, X-linked ACTH, adreno-corticotrophin; LH, luteinising hormone; TSH, thyrotrophin; FSH, follicle-stimulating hormone; TRH, thyrotrophin-releasing hormone; GRH, growth hormone-releasing hormone; GNRH, gonadotropin-releasing hormone; PTH, parathyroid hormone

classic negative feedback system controlling calcium sensing in the parathyroid cell has the unique feature that the agonist is an ion (Ca^{2+}). PTH secreted by the cell acts on bone and kidney to increase serum Ca^{2+}, which in turn controls PTH secretion via the cell surface receptor (Fig. 3). The receptor is not an ion channel, but a GPCR belonging to the metabotropic glutamate receptor subfamily. It is unique in having many acidic residues and conserved cysteine residues, and in being highly glycosylated (Brown *et al.* 1993).

The normal parathyroid cell (Fig. 3, left) has two functional alleles of the calcium receptor. Heterozygous loss of receptor function mutations in the parathyroid and kidney in FHH result in mildly increased serum Ca^{2+} and hypocalciuria. Many calcium receptor mutations have been described (Brown *et al.* 1998). In the homozygote or compound heterozygote, loss of both normal receptor alleles results in severe hypercalcaemia, severe PTH elevation with bone demineralisation, and hypocalciuria (Fig. 3, right). This is NSPH, an emergency that requires surgical parathyroidectomy.

However, some anomalies have emerged in relation to these disorders. Autosomal dominant inheritance of a paternal mutation with a normal mother can cause hyperparathyroidism *in utero* because of inappropriate fetal perception of the mother's normal calcium level as hypocalcaemia.

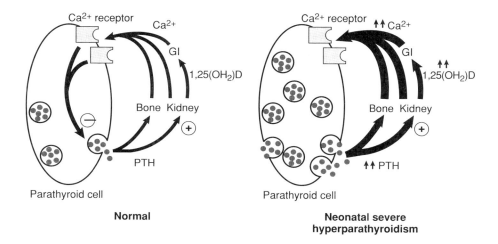

Figure 3 Calcium receptor pathways in parathyroid cells with normal and mutant receptors. Left: the normal cell has two functional alleles of the calcium receptor. Right: loss of both normal receptor alleles results in neonatal severe hyperparathyroidism (NSPH), with severe hypercalcaemia, severe PTH elevation, bone demineralisation and hypocalciuria.

This condition is transient and does not need surgical correction, and so must be recognised and distinguished from NSPH (Brown *et al.* 1998). In addition, *de novo* heterozygous calcium-sensing receptor mutations may cause NSPH through a dominant negative effect (Brown *et al.* 1998).

GPCR gain-of-function mutations

GPCR gain-of-function mutations and associated disorders are listed in Table 3. The first such mutation to be identified was autosomal familial male precocious puberty. This disorder, sporadic hyperfunctional thyroid nodules, familial non-autoimmune hyperthyroidism and others are caused by constitutively activating mutations, in which expressed receptors are active in the absence of their agonists (Shenker *et al.* 1993).

Gain-of-function mutations in the CaR cause autosomal dominant hypoparathyroidism with hypercalcaemia. Most occur in the heavily glycosylated extracellular domain and cause calcium hypersensitivity rather than constitutive activation; however, we have recently identified a mutation on the 7th transmembrane domain of the CaR that does cause constitutive activation (Spiegel, unpublished observations).

Table 3 Disorders caused by GPCR gain-of-function mutations (Spiegel 1998)

Receptor	Disorder	Inheritance*
Rhodopsin	congenital night blindness	D
LH	familial male precocious puberty	D
TSH	sporadic hyperfunctional thyroid nodules/	S
	familial non-autoimmune hyperthyroidism	D
CaR	familial hypoparathyroidism	D
PTH/PTHrP	Jansen metaphyseal chondrodysplasia	D
FSH	gonadotrophin-independent spermatogenesis	D

D, autosomal dominant; S, somatic; LH, luteinising hormone; TSH, thyrotrophin; PTH, parathyroid hormone; FSH, follicle-stimulating hormone

Conclusions and the future

- Several examples of loss- and gain-of-function mutations in GPCR and G-protein α-subunits have been reviewed, together with the disorders they cause.
- Our studies on the structure and function of the CaR are helping to define the molecular basis for disorders of calcium metabolism, and to suggest novel therapeutic approaches.
- Mutations in other components of G-protein signalling pathways relevant to disease will be discovered. A German group already reporting association of hypertension with a variant of the β3 subtype of β-subunit in G-proteins (Siffert *et al.* 1998).
- Gene sequence variations (polymorphisms) are being investigated that do not represent disease-causing mutations, but will nevertheless be critical in the inheritance of complex diseases.
- For example, one chemokine receptor – CCR5 – is the cell-surface entry point for HIV, and individuals with inactivating sequence variations of this receptor are completely resistant to the virus. I believe that many other examples will emerge.
- Future studies of the CaR and other GCPRs are likely to reveal additional mutations and polymorphisms relevant to human diseases.

References

Albright F, Burnett CH, Smith PH 1942 Pseudohypoparathyroidism – an example of 'Seabright-Bantam syndrome'. *Endocrinology* **30** 922–932.
Brown EM, Gamba G, Riccardi D *et al.* 1993 Cloning and characterization of an extracellular Ca^{2+}-sensing receptor from bovine parathyroid. *Nature* **366** 575–580.

Brown EM, Pollak M, Hebert SC 1998 The extracellular calcium-sensing receptor: its role in health and disease. *Annual Review of Medicine* **49** 15–29.

Buck L, Axel R 1991 A novel multigene family may encode odorant receptors: a molecular basis for odorant recognition. *Cell* **65** 175–178.

Chase LR, Melson GL, Aurbach GD 1969 Pseudohypoparathyroidism: defective excretion of 3′,5′-AMP in response to parathyroid hormone. *Journal of Clinical Investigation* **48** 1832–1844.

Davies SJ, Hughes HE 1993 Imprinting in Albright's hereditary osteodystrophy. *Journal of Medical Genetics* **30** 101–103.

Dohlman HG, Thorner J 1997 RGS proteins and signaling by heterotrimeric G-proteins. *Journal of Biological Chemistry* **272** 3871–3874.

Kozasa T, Jiang X, Hart MJ, Sternweis PM, Singer WD, Gilman AG *et al.* 1998 p115 Rho GEF, a GTP-ase activating-protein for $G\alpha_{12}$ and $G\alpha_{13}$. *Science* **280** 1209–2114.

Levine MA, Downs RW Jr, Singer M, Marx SJ, Aurbach GD, Speigel AM *et al.* 1980 Deficient activity of guanine nucleotide regulatory protein in erythrocytes from patients with pseudohypoparathyroidism. *Biochemical and Biophysical Research Communications* **94** 1319–1324.

Shenker A, Laue L, Kosugi S, Merendino JJ Jr, Minegishi T, Cutler GB Jr *et al.* 1993 A constitutively activating mutation of the luteinizing hormone receptor in familial male precocious puberty. *Nature* **265** 652–654.

Siffert W, Rosskopf D, Siffert G, Busch S, Moritz A, Erbel E *et al.* 1998 Association of a human G-protein β^3 subunit variant with hypertension. *Nature Genetics* **18** 45–48.

Spiegel AM (ed.) 1998 *G-proteins, Receptors, and Disease*. Totawa NJ: Humana Press,

Weinstein LS 1998 Albright hereditary osteodystrophy, pseudohypoparathyroidism and G_s deficiency. In *G-proteins, Receptors, and Disease*, pp 23–56. Ed. Spiegel AM. Totawa NJ: Humana Press.

Weinstein LS, Shenker A, Gejman PV, Merino MJ, Friedman E, Speigel AM *et al.* 1991 Activating mutations of the stimulatory G-protein in the McCune–Albright syndrome. *New England Journal of Medicine* **325** 1688–1695.

Yu S, Yu D, Lee E, Eckhaus M, Lee R, Corria Z *et al.* 1998 Variable and tissue-specific hormone resistance in heterotrimeric G_s-protein α-subunits ($G_s\alpha$) knockout mice is due to tissue-specific imprinting of the $G_s\alpha$ gene. *Proceedings of the Academy of Sciences of the USA* **95** 8715–8720.

Overgrowth syndromes

Genetic Insights in Paediatric Endocrinology and Metabolism
Eds S O'Rahilly and D B Dunger
BioScientifica Ltd, Bristol (1999)

A clinical overview of overgrowth syndromes

J Clayton-Smith

Regional Genetic Service, St Mary's Hospital, Hathersage Road, Manchester, M13 0JH, UK

Giants have often been recorded in history. Elucidating some disorders within the group of overgrowth syndromes can help clinicians understand the mechanisms – and failure – of growth regulation. Overgrowth occurs by way of increases in cell size or cell number (hypertrophy or hyperplasia). Traditionally it has been classified as primary or secondary to an identifiable cause, but this classification becomes less useful as more causes of overgrowth are being identified. A more useful division is into generalised, localised and tissue-specific overgrowth. This chapter focuses on the clinical presentation of some rare overgrowth syndromes, the study of which is vital for a better understanding of the multiple factors involved in growth regulation.

Endocrine disorders and overgrowth

Defects of the hypothalamo–pituitary–adrenal axis

Defective pathways between the pituitary and adrenals can result in a decrease in corticosteroid production and an increase in levels of androgenic steroids, leading to overgrowth.

The commonest such condition is congenital adrenal hyperplasia (CAH), but a rarer condition is caused by adrenocorticotrophin (ACTH) resistance due to a receptor mutation. This is characterised by tall stature, long tapering fingers and hyperpigmentation of the skin, tongue and buccal mucosa (Slavotinek *et al.* 1998).

Berardinelli lipodystrophy

This is a disorder of insulin binding, characterised by increased early skeletal growth and bone density, reduced body fat, lipodystrophy, prominent muscles, acanthosis nigricans, large genitalia, hirsutism and diabetes (Moller & Flier 1991).

Sanfillipo syndrome (MPS III)

This metabolic cause of overgrowth is often overlooked because of the relatively mild dysmorphic features. A deficiency of one or more of the enzymes in the heparan sulphate pathway leads to the accumulation of this metabolite in the lysosomes. Four separate enzyme defects have been recognised (Wraith 1995). Children with this syndrome often develop normally until school age. They then suffer progressive loss of skills and may present with behavioural problems. They have mild facial coarsening, abundant scalp hair and generalised overgrowth in early life, although this is not maintained in later childhood and adult life. Corneal clouding and hepatosplenomegaly are usually absent.

McCune–Albright syndrome

McCune-Albright syndrome is caused by a mosaic-activating mutation affecting GS-a (Shenker *et al*. 1994). Patients present with skin hyperpigmentation that has a 'coast of Maine' border, distinguishing it from the smooth-bordered café-au-lait patches of neurofibromatosis. Polyostotic fibrous dysplasia leads to pathological fractures, and early overgrowth is followed by precocious puberty, resulting in subnormal final height.

Multiple congenital abnormality syndromes associated with overgrowth

Beckwith–Wiedemann syndrome (BWS) phenotypes

The genetics and molecular pathology of this syndrome are discussed in detail in the next chapter, but an account is included here to assist comparisons with the other overgrowth syndromes described. The three major features of BWS are pre- and postnatal overgrowth, exomphalos and macroglossia.

The placenta is very large and the pregnancy is often complicated by polyhydramnios leading to premature delivery. Because effects on the placenta are a feature of this and other overgrowth syndromes, the placentae of overgrown babies have an important part to play in research into overgrowth. They should be carefully examined and not, as often happens, disposed of immediately after the birth.

Several other features are associated with BWS. Neonatal hypoglycaemia and polycythaemia occur; organomegaly particularly affects the kidneys, which are histologically immature. Children with BWS have a characteristic facies, with naevus flammeus and flattened malar regions, along with posterior ear pits and creases across the lobes; some show hemihypertrophy associated with a predisposition to embryonal tumours (e.g. Wilms tumour, which occurs in 2–5% of affected children) (Elliot *et al.* 1994). With hemi-hypertrophy, differing leg lengths can lead to scoliosis, and differing foot sizes to practical difficulties in shoe buying.

There are many reports of affected monozygotic twins, usually girls, who are often phenotypically discordant for BWS (Clayton-Smith *et al.* 1992). A pair of such twins followed at our clinic had almost lost their BWS phenotype by around 6 years of age. Their growth also normalised, and affected individuals are generally not particularly tall at final height. This agrees with observations that *IGF2* gene expression is greater in embryonic and early life than it is later (Ohlssen *et al.* 1993).

BWS is associated with biallelic over-expression of *IGF2*, an imprinted gene expressed only from the paternal chromosome 11 (Reik *et al.* 1995). This can occur by paternal duplication of chromosome 11p15.5, uniparental disomy of chromosome 11, maternal chromosome rearrangement involving 11p15.5 or by mutations within the p57^{KIP2} gene at 11p15.5. Some phenotype–genotype correlation occurs in BWS (Henry *et al.* 1993). For example: duplication of 11p15.5 tends to be associated with mental retardation, congenital heart disease, cleft lip and palate and other multiple abnormalities; Henry suggested that patients with UPD 11 are more likely to have hemihypertrophy and neoplasia; and those with p57^{KIP2} defects have a lower risk of neoplasia and overgrowth, but a much higher incidence of exomphalos than the other groups (Hatada *et al.* 1996). Contrary to formerly accepted opinion, our own observations confirm that intellectual development is fairly normal in uncomplicated BWS, with the exception of some patients with Dup 11p15.5.

Non-syndromal overgrowth and BWS

Non-syndromal overgrowth with overexpression of IGF-II has recently been reported in a Polynesian population (Morison *et al.* 1996). They were non-dysmorphic, very large, and had renal histology resembling that of BWS, with immature glomeruli. Some presented with Wilms tumour early in life. It may be relevant that birthweights greater than 4 kg are over-represented among cohorts of children presenting with Wilms tumour. It appears that a continuum exists between the full-blown BWS on one hand and IGF-II overexpression without overt dysmorphic features but with some renal BWS characteristics, on the other.

Simpson–Golabi–Behmel syndrome (SGBS)

The features of SGBS and BWS show considerable overlap; in both, affected children have pre- and postnatal overgrowth, organomegaly and an increased risk of embryonal tumours, particularly Wilms tumour (Verloes *et al.* 1995). In addition, SGBS patients may have diaphragmatic hernia, polydactyly, supernumerary nipples and mild learning difficulties. Other dysmorphic features that may occur in SGBS include: macrocephaly; a prominent metopic suture, long, thin upper lip, cleft lip and palate, and macroglossia with a prominent midline groove and tongue-tie; a narrow chest with a pectus excavatum or carinatum deformity; 'squared-off' hands with clinodactyly and, curiously, hypoplasia of the index finger nail. Adults with SGBS show overgrowth, the average final height for males being around 2 m. One of our adult male subjects is 2.07 m tall, has a prominent jaw, a pectus deformity and left ventricular hypertrophy, another feature of SGBS which can lead to conduction defects and arrhythmias.

SGBS is associated with mutations in the glypican gene *GPC3* at Xq25-27 (Pilia *et al.* 1996). Glypican is a cell-surface proteoglycan highly expressed in mesodermal embryonic tissues, which explains the marked overgrowth effects in the placenta and neonate. Interactions between *GPC3* and *IGF2* – perhaps involving receptor competition – have been proposed, which could explain the overlap in the features of SGBS and BWS (Weksberg *et al.* 1996).

Despite the overlap, it is essential for effective counselling that clinicians distinguish the two syndromes. The X-linked SGBS carries a much higher risk of recurrence than BWS, and is associated with more congenital malformations.

Sotos syndrome

This condition is probably overdiagnosed. It is associated with accelerated linear growth and advanced bone age in childhood. Affected individuals have very large heads, hands and feet, a characteristic facies and marked joint laxity with hypotonia. Contrary to what was formerly accepted, not all individuals with Sotos syndrome are intellectually impaired, but the range of IQ is very wide: 18–119 (Cole & Hughes 1990). Reports of increased incidence of solid tumours in this condition probably represent biased reporting (Cole & Hughes 1990).

In Sotos syndrome the face tends to be long, with a prominent chin, high hairline and large head circumference. High colour over the cheekbones and a red nose are good diagnostic features. Growth partially normalises with age, final height being about 10 cm above normal expected height, and the pointed chin becomes more prominent.

Weaver syndrome

This condition is often classified along with Sotos syndrome. Again it is associated with pre- and postnatal overgrowth, advanced bone age with disharmonious maturation between different bones, a characteristic facies with a small receding chin, macrocephaly, developmental delay, flexion contractures of the fingers and splayed metaphyses. Weaver syndrome is not known to be associated with an increased risk of neoplasia.

Localised overgrowth syndromes

Localised overgrowth may occur alone, as in isolated hemihypertrophy, or as part of other conditions (e.g. Proteus syndrome).

Isolated hemihypertrophy

Children with this not infrequent condition have hemihypertrophy without other congenital abnormalities and their development is otherwise entirely normal, although their predisposition to Wilms and other embryonal tumours must be borne in mind by the managing physician (Mark 1994).

Proteus syndrome

The famous 'elephant man', Joseph Merrick, did not suffer from neurofibromatosis, as has been suggested, but from Proteus syndrome (Tibbles & Cohen 1986). The characteristic connective tissue overgrowth results in cerebriform 'moccasin' plantar hyperplasia, connective tissue and linear verrucous naevi in the skin, vascular naevi and sometimes massive hyperostoses.

The hyperplasias are irregular, sporadic and relentlessly progressive throughout life, so that an apparently normal child will develop isolated areas of overgrowth which become increasingly severe. Proteus syndrome is thought to be a lethal mutation in which the affected individual survives because of mosaicism (see below), as in the activating mutations of McCune–Albright syndrome. In the occasional case of segmental Proteus syndrome, however, the characteristic hyperplastic changes occur in a segmental distribution.

Hemihyperplasia lipomatosis

Hemihyperplasia lipomatosis is sometimes confused with Proteus syndrome, but the overgrowth remains in proportion, so that the child develops a 'scaled-up' version of a limb, extremity or digit. Klippel–Trenauney–Weber syndrome is another similar sporadic condition which, like Proteus syndrome, is probably a lethal mutation surviving by mosaicism (Happle 1990).

Haemangioma

Strawberry haemangioma and vascular malformations (e.g. the typical 'strawberry' mark) are typically not present at birth but progressively develop over the first few years of life and then undergo spontaneous involution; the mechanisms of this natural history are still obscure. Haemangiomata are quite common, occurring in about 1/100 neonates, and most are benign. However, they can be troublesome if their position or rapid growth interferes with the airway or affects functions such as eyesight. Basic fibroblast growth factor (bFGF) is overexpressed within haemangiomata. However, treatment with interferon-a resulting in regression of steroid-refractory haemangiomata also lowers urinary levels of bFGF mRNA in patients' urine (Ezekowitz *et al.* 1999).

Mosaicism and overgrowth

Mosaicism is the coexistence of two or more differing cell types within the body tissues. There are several possible causes of overgrowth accompanied by mosaicism. The specific mutation leading to overgrowth is active in the affected cells, or the overgrowth may be a consequence of mosaicism itself. The latter appears quite likely in view of the existence of mosaic phenotypes associated with both under- and overgrowth. Clinical features of mosaicism include asymmetry, hemihypertrophy, syndactyly and abnormalities of skin pigmentation. These latter often follow Blaschko's lines, the primitive fusion lines of the skin that run along the limbs and round the trunk. Perhaps the best examples of such mosaicism generally seen are the diploid-triploid mosaics, in which cells with 46 and 69 chromosomes are mixed (Donnai *et al.* 1988). Mosaicism may also have a direct effect on placental function leading to under- or overgrowth.

Other forms of chromosomal mosaicism give rise to generalised overgrowth. For example, one of our patients was a large, very hypotonic baby with fronto-temporal balding and a prominent philtrum who had 12p tetrasomy, with four copies of the short arm of chromosome 12. This is another disorder that survives only in mosaic form.

The sporadic condition known as cutis marmorata-macrocephaly syndrome has been defined only recently. Late development of skin hyperpigmentation following Blaschko's lines suggests that it is a mosaic/overgrowth phenomenon. In addition to its marbled appearance, the skin is 'doughy'-textured, apparently due to soft-tissue overgrowth. Patients also have a box-shaped head and often have a philtral abnormality. Other typical features include 2/3 syndactyly of the toes, 3/4 syndactyly of the fingers, and internal arterio-venous malformations. Many affected children have large heads at birth, and the head size continues to increase reaching a size of greater than 60 cm in many cases (Clayton-Smith *et al.* 1997).

Overgrowth, neoplasia and screening

Increased susceptibility to embryonal tumours is a feature of several overgrowth syndromes, and IGF-II expression is known to be increased in some of these tumours (Ogawa *et al.* 1993). Consequently, screening for malignancies – Wilms tumour in particular – is warranted for cases in which a predisposition is suspected. Current screening practice in our own centre includes regular 6-monthly ultrasound scanning and abdominal palpation. Screening should continue until growth has ceased and the risk of Wilms tumour has declined. It should be noted that we have observed the development of a Wilms tumour in a patient as old as 12 years.

Conclusions and the future

- Among common factors emerging among the overgrowth syndromes described here are *IGF2* overexpression and somatic mosaicism.
- Little is understood about the genetic aetiology of many of these syndromes – Sotos syndrome, which has long been recognised, being a good example.
- Many more such overgrowth syndromes remain to be recognised and elucidated.
- Further research into these syndromes is crucial for the better understanding of the various factors involved in growth regulation.

References

Clayton-Smith J, Kerr B, Brunner H, Tranebjaerg L, Magee AK & Hennekam R *et al.* 1997 Macrocephaly with cutis marmorata, haemangioma and syndactyly – a distinctive overgrowth syndrome. *Clinical Dysmorphology* 6 291–302.

Clayton-Smith J, Read AP & Donnai D 1992 Monozygotic twinning and Wiedemann-Beckwith syndrome. *American Journal of Medical Genetics* **42** 633–637.

Cole TRP & Hughes HE 1990 Syndrome of the month. Sotos syndrome. *Journal of Medical Genetics* **27** 571–576.

Donnai D, Read AP, McKeown C & Andrews T 1988 Hypomelanosis of Ito: a manifestation of mosaicism or chimerism? *Journal of Medical Genetics* **25** 809–818.

Elliot M, Bayly R, Cole T *et al.* 1994 Clinical feature and natural history of Beckwith-Wiedemann syndrome: presentation of 74 new cases. *Clinical Genetics* **46** 168–174.

Ezekowitz A, Mulliken J & Folkman J 1999 Interferon alpha therapy of haemangiomas in newborns and infants. *British Journal of Haematology* **79** (suppl) 67–68.

Happle R 1993 Klippel-Trenauney syndrome: is it a paradominant trait? *British Journal of Dermatology* **128** 465.

Hatada I, Ohashi H & Fukushma Y 1996 An imprinted gene is mutated in Beckwith-Wiedemann syndrome. *Nature Genetics* **14** 171–173.

Henry I, Puech A & Riesewijk A 1993 Somatic mosaicism for partial paternal isodisomy in Wiedemann Beckwith syndrome: a post-fertilisation event. *European Journal of Human Genetics* **1** 19–29.

Mark S 1994 A virilized patient with congenital hemihypertrophy. *Postgraduate Medical Journal* **70** 752–755.

Moller DE & Flier JS 1991 Insulin resistance-mechanism, syndromes, and implications. *New England Journal of Medicine* **325** 938–948.

Morison IM, Becroft DM, Taniguchi T, Woods CA & Reeve AE 1996 Somatic overgrowth associated with over-expression of insulin-like growth factor II. *Nature Medicine* **2** 311–316.

Ogawa O, Becroft DM, Morison IM *et al.* 1993 Constitutional relaxation of insulin-like growth factor II gene imprinting associated with Wilms tumour and gigantism. *Nature Genetics* **5** 408–412.

Ohlssen R, Nystrom A & Pfeifer-Ohlsson S 1993 IGF2 is parentally imprinted during human embryogenesis and in the Beckwith-Wiedemann syndrome. *Nature Genetics* **4** 94–97.

Pilia G, Schlessinger D, Hughes-Benzie RM *et al.* 1996 Mutations in GPC3, a glypican gene, cause the Simpson-Golabi-Behmel overgrowth syndrome. *Nature Genetics* **12** 241–247.

Reik W, Brown KW, Schneid H, Le Bouly, Bickmore W & Maher EH 1995 Imprinting mutations in the Beckwith-Wiedemann syndrome suggested by an altered imprinting pattern in the IGF2 - H19 domain. *Human Molecular Genetics* **4** 2379–2385.

Shenker A, Weinstein LS, Sweet DE & Spiegel AM 1994 An activating GS alpha mutation is present in fibrous dysplasia of bone in the McCune Albright syndrome. *Journal of Clinical Endocrinology and Metabolism* **79** 750–755.

Slavotinek AM, Hurst JA, Dunger D & Wilkie AO 1998 ACTH receptor mutation in a girl with familial glucocorticoid deficiency. *Clinical Genetics* 1998 **53** 57–62.

Tibbles JAR & Cohen MMJR 1986 The Proteus syndrome: the Elephant Man diagnosed. *British Medical Journal* **26** 683–684.

Verloes A, Massart B & Dehalleux I 1995 Clinical overlap of Beckwith-Wiedemann, Periman and Simpson-Golabi-Behmel syndromes: a diagnostic pitfall. *Clinical Genetics* **47** 257–262.

Weksberg R, Squire JA & Templeton DM 1996 Glypicans: a growing trend. *Nature Genetics* **12** 225–227.

Wraith JE 1995 The mucopolysaccharidoses: a clinical review and guide to management. *Archives of Diseases of Childhood* **72** 263–267.

Genetic Insights in Paediatric Endocrinology and Metabolism
Eds S O'Rahilly and D B Dunger
BioScientifica Ltd, Bristol (1999)

Beckwith–Wiedemann syndrome

E R Maher

Section of Medical and Molecular Genetics, Department of Paediatrics and
Child Health, University of Birmingham, Birmingham, B15 2TT, UK

This chapter presents an overview of studies on the complex genetics and molecular pathology of Beckwith–Wiedemann syndrome (BWS). Investigations of BWS are providing insights into some of the molecular elements involved in genomic imprinting. The chapter by Clayton-Smith provides a concise overview of BWS. Investigations of BWS have concentrated on the cluster of imprinted genes located at the end of the short arm of chromosome 11 (11p15) in humans and chromosome 7 in mice (including the IGF2 and H19 genes).

Clinical features of BWS

BWS is an overgrowth disorder associated with a variety of congenital anomalies (e.g. overgrowth, macroglossia) and a susceptibility to embryonal tumours in 5% of cases (Elliott & Maher 1994).

Genetic features of BWS

The extreme clinical variability of BWS is paralleled by its genetic heterogeneity. Three major subgroups may be distinguished.

- *Chromosomal aberrations* affecting about 2% of patients include paternally derived duplications of distal 11p15.5 and maternally derived balanced rearrangements such as inversions or translocations which involve two major regions: BWS cluster regions (BWSCR) 1 and 2.
- *Familial BWS* (about 15%) is dominantly transmitted, with a maternal transmission effect.
- *Sporadic occurrence*, accounting for most cases of BWS, involves uniparental (paternal) isodisomy in about one-fifth of patients.

Each of these subtypes implicates imprinted genes, which in the human are located in distal chromosome 11 (Reik & Maher 1997). The involvement of imprinting is also suggested by the results of systematic familial studies,

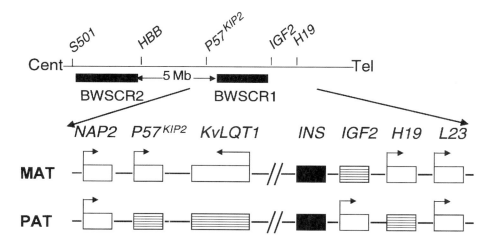

Figure 1 The chromosome 11p15 gene cluster involved in BWS and their transcription (arrows) from maternal and/or paternal alleles. Imprinting of the insulin (INS) gene has not been demonstrated in man. (Adapted from Reik & Maher 1997.)

showing more complete penetrance with maternal transmission (Reik & Maher 1997).

The major genes in the imprinted 11p15 cluster which may be involved in BWS are shown in Fig. 1. Linkage analysis and molecular cytogenetic studies have indicated that the 11p15.5 region contains a locus or loci for BWS; in addition to IGF2 and H19 this region contains the p57[KIP2] (CDKN1C) and KvLQT1 (KCNQ1) genes.

At the telomeric end of this region lies the L23 gene, which is not imprinted and is biallelically expressed; the same applies to NAP2 at the centromeric end. Between them lie several imprinted genes that are, or may be, relevant to BWS. The cyclin-dependent kinase inhibitor gene p57[KIP2] is almost exclusively maternally expressed in humans. The growth promoter IGF-II (insulin-like growth factor-II) is paternally expressed, and close to it (about 100 kb) is the maternally expressed H19; this gene encodes an mRNA which does not encode a protein.

The KvLQT1 gene is involved in a number of genetic disorders. Dominant mutations in this gene give rise to the long QT syndrome, and recessive mutations are associated with Jervell–Lange–Nielsen syndrome, which causes deafness and long QT. Inversions and translocations in BWS have been mapped to two regions in chromosome 11p15, BWSCR1 and

BWSCR1. All the breakpoints in BWSCR1 interrupt KvLQT1, which has in consequence been proposed as a candidate BWS gene (Lee *et al.* 1997*b*). However, to date no KvLQT1 mutations have been found in BWS. This gene demonstrates tissue-specific imprinting; it is expressed biallelically in the heart, but elsewhere only maternally. Some inversions and translocations in BWS map through BWSCR2, but this region has been less well studied.

Studies on BWS

The Birmingham–Cambridge study

The aims of our study (Reik & Maher *et al.* 1997) have been to investigate the molecular pathology of BWS in a large cohort of patients, to elucidate the role of candidate genes IGF2, H19 and p57^{KIP2}, and to ascertain whether differences in phenotypic expression are associated with different molecular mechanisms.

No formal diagnostic criteria existed for BWS, so we adopted the following, which are more stringent than those used by some other groups. BWS was diagnosed if the patient had three major diagnostic features, or two major together with three minor features. Major features included an abdominal wall defect, macroglossia, and pre- or postnatal overgrowth (>90th centile). Minor features were ear creases and pits, facial naevus flammeus, neonatal hypoglycaemia, nephromegaly and hemihypertrophy (Elliott & Maher 1994).

This work was begun following published reports of paternal uniparental disomy (UPD) of chromosome 11p51.5 in patients with sporadic BWS (Henri *et al.* 1991). In BWS, this phenomenon is always the result of mitotic recombination, and the child is mosaic for UPD (paternal isodisomy). In the largest such study in the literature, 83 out of 106 BWS patients (78%) were informative at the TH or IGF-II locus for UPD analysis. Of these, 69 (83%) showed normal inheritance and the remaining 14 (17%) had paternal isodisomy and were mosaic. No patient with heterodisomy was found (Slatter *et al.* 1994).

Our disomy studies have confirmed the role of imprinted genes in BWS. We also hoped that identifying patients with partial isodisomy (when disomy is restricted to part of chromosome 11) would help us to discriminate candidate genes (Fig. 1) involved and not involved in BWS. However, this was not achieved, as the minimal disomic region included all of the chromosome 11p15.5 imprinted cluster (Catchpoole *et al.* 1997).

Mechanisms of overgrowth in BWS patients with disomy

It could be postulated that overgrowth results from a deficiency of maternally expressed growth-repressors such as p57[KIP2] and H19, or a paternal excess of IGF-II. Our early studies on the role of IGF-II in BWS were undertaken because of evidence that this growth factor is involved in the condition: IGF-II is a paternally expressed growth promoter mapping to chromosome 11p15.5; correlations have been found between tissue types affected in BWS and the sites of most abundant IGF-II expression; paternal UPD and duplication of 11p15.5 result in increased effective gene dosage of IGF2 (Reik & Maher 1997).

The H19 gene, hypermethylation and loss of imprinting of IGF-II in sporadic BWS

Although the function of the H19 gene is not yet known, reciprocal imprinting of IGF2 and H19 has been reported in the mouse. An 'enhancer competition model' has been proposed in which a common enhancer of both IGF2 and H19 interacts on the maternal allele preferentially with the H19 promoter, resulting in maternal transcription and expression of H19 RNA but not of IGF2. The theory also proposes that, on the paternal allele, the H19 promoter is methylated and unavailable to the enhancer element, so that IGF2 is preferentially expressed. This hypothesis is supported by the reported biallelic expression of IGF2 in transgenic mice bearing various H19 deletions (Leighton *et al.* 1995).

In addition, H19 methylation analysis using methylation-sensitive restriction digests in BWS patients has detected hypermethylation of H19 in some BWS (Reik *et al.* 1995, Catchpoole *et al.* 1997). The normal ratio of alleles showing a methylated and an unmethylated H19 promoter region should be about 1:1 (methylation index 0.5). However, among a series of 80 sporadic BWS cases, all patients with UPD showed hypermethylation (methylation index >0.6); this reflected their mosaic status, with most cells having two paternal alleles. Surprisingly increased methylation was also detected in 5/63 (8%) of non-UPD cases of BWS. In these patients hypermethylation was associated with methylation of, and loss of imprinting in, maternal IGF2, resulting in biallelic expression of IGF2 and silencing of maternal H19 expression (Reik *et al.* 1995). These findings recall those in the transgenic mouse models with H19 deletions, and are suggestive of an imprinting centre defect. The pattern of IGF2 and H19 expression in unaffected and BWS patients is shown diagrammatically in Fig. 2.

It has been shown that only a minority of patients with BWS have H19 hypermethylation, but it has been known since 1993 that loss of imprinting

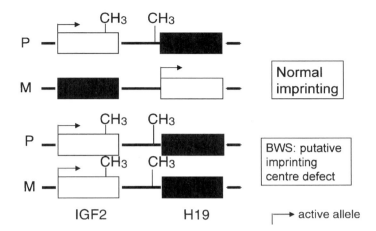

Figure 2 Imprinting centre (BWS-IC1) defects in BWS. **Upper** In unaffected individuals IGF-II is expressed and H19 silenced on the paternal allele, *vice versa* for the maternal allele. **Lower** Both alleles in BWS patients with H19 hypermethylation express IGF-II but not H19, so that the maternal chromosome mimics a paternal chromosome. (Adapted from Reik & Maher 1997.)

of IGF2 with biallelic expression is fairly common in BWS (Weksberg *et al.* 1993). But more recently we found that 9/11 BWS patients with normal H19 methylation and normal chromosomes showed loss of IGF2 imprinting along with biallelic IGF expression, and postulated that they had an H19-independent pathway to loss of IGF2 imprinting (Joyce *et al.* 1997). Further knowledge of the IGF2 gene is necessary to understand what the mechanism of this might be.

Control of imprinting in BWS

The complex IGF2 gene has four promoters. Promoter P1 is not imprinted, is biallelically expressed and is active mainly in adult tissues, including the liver. Promoters P2, P3 and P4 are used mainly in developing tissues and are all imprinted. Hence one possible mechanism for loss of imprinting is a switch from P2–P4 to P1 activity, although this does not in fact occur, and IGF2 loss of imprinting appears to result from loss of imprinting at P2–P4 (Joyce *et al.* 1997). The definitive evidence for an H19-independent mechanism of loss of imprinting has come from the study of a single rare family which had an inversion of chromosome 11 with a break point in distal chromosome 11p15.5. The grandmother was known not to be a carrier of the inversion and father was unavailable for analysis, but the apparently normal mother was a carrier and passed the inversion on to her two children, both of whom had BWS. The breakpoint was mapped to within BWSCR1, about 200 kb centromeric to IGF2. IGF2 imprinting was found to be lost, with IGF-II expression by the maternal allele, in the presence of normal H19 methylation and expression (Brown *et al.* 1996), confirming the existence an H19-independent mechanism for loss of imprinting.

We have proposed that two separate BWS imprinting centres (BWS-ICs) exist: one (BWS-IC1) exerting control locally over H19 and IGF2; and a second (BWS-IC2) located in the KvLQT1 region. BWS-IC2 would be either disrupted directly by a translocation or inversion, or simply map centromeric to the breakpoint; it would affect IGF2 imprinting, but not H19 imprinting. Finding of loss of imprinting with production of an antisense mRNA within an intron of the KvLQT1 gene in a fetus with BWS, expressed by the paternal allele but not by the methylated maternal gene, represented supporting evidence for our model. Further very recent imprinting studies are also in keeping with the predictions of our model (Smilinich *et al.* in press)

Thus, most patients with sporadic BWS without UPD have loss of imprinting at IGF2, which is detectable at P1–P4. This loss of imprinting may be associated with: normal H19 imprinting (normal H19/IGF2 methylation); or silencing of H19 together with either hyper- or normal H19 methylation. So IGF2 loss of imprinting may be caused by multiple mechanisms that are H19-dependent or -independent (Joyce *et al.* 1997).

p57^{KIP2} and BWS

Germline mutations of p57^{KIP2} were first reported by Hatada *et al.* (1996), but the frequencies of p57^{KIP2} mutations reported by different groups differ widely, from 0% to 20%, probably reflecting patient selection criteria and whether sporadic or familial BWS was studied (Hatada *et al.* 1997, Lee *et al.* 1997*a*, O'Keefe *et al.* 1997, Okamoto *et al.* 1998). We sequenced the coding regions of the gene and identified mutations that differed from those reported in the literature. In all informative inherited cases the parent of origin was the mother. Mutations have been found in all three of the p57^{KIP2} protein domains – the cyclin-dependent kinase inhibitor, Pro-Ala repeat, and a further domain (QT) of unknown function. Overall, our recorded incidence of p57^{KIP2} coding mutations was only 4% (2/54) in sporadic BWS, but 43% (3/7) in familial kindreds (Lam *et al.* in press).

Genotype-phenotype correlations

Do p57^{KIP2} mutations cause BWS directly, or via effects on IGF2/H19 imprinting? Our evidence suggests the former mechanism, as there is no effect on IGF2/H19 methylation. BWS is a highly heterogeneous disorder, but subgroups have been defined by molecular typing (Table 1) (Reik & Maher 1997), and we have detected correlation between the molecular subgroups and specific BWS phenotypes. Three major molecular subgroups characterised are p57^{KIP2} mutations, UPD, and biallelic IGF2 expression in the presence of H19 hypermethylation due to a BWS-IC1 defect.

Table 1 Imprinting analysis in BWS patients

	Normal karyotype				Maternally inherited rearrangement	Paternal UPD
IGF-II expression	monoallelic	biallelic	biallelic	biallelic	biallelic	2 × monoallelic
H19 expression	normal	none	normal	none	normal	none (2 × monoallelic)
IGF-II methylation	normal	?	normal	altered	normal	2 × monoallelic
H19 methylation	normal	normal	normal	altered	normal	2 × monoallelic
Replication timing	?	?	?	normal	altered	altered
Frequency	16%	18%	36%	5–10%	1%	20%

Our chief observations on genotype–phenotype correlations were as follows.
- UPD and hemihypertrophy were strongly correlated (probably because the degree of mosaicism on each side of the body is different).
- The previously suggested strong association between UPD and increased risk of Wilms tumour was not detected.
- Exomphalos was much more common among patients with p57^{KIP2} mutations (11/13) than in those with BWS-IC1 defects (0/5; $P < 0.005$) or UPD (0/9; $P < 0.005$).
- Neoplasms have not yet been found in BWS associated with p57^{KIP2} mutations.

Animal studies and human BWS

Although we are cautious in interpreting the results of our studies on small numbers of patients, they do accord with findings from mouse models of

BWS. For example, the p57^{KIP2} knockout model shows anterior abdominal wall defects (Zhang *et al.* 1997) and the IGF2 overexpression model demonstrates overgrowth and macroglossia (Sun *et al.* 1997). Skeletal abnormalities occur in both models. The differences suggest that the current explanation for exomphalos – failure of abdominal wall closure as a mechanical consequence of organomegaly – may not be true. In humans, similar (but not identical) phenotypes may result from the loss of p57^{KIP2} and IGF2 overexpression. We suspect that p57^{KIP2} and IGF-II operate on different points in the same growth control pathway, resulting in overlapping but not identical phenotypes.

Conclusions and the future

- BWS is a human imprinting disorder that is clinically variable and genetically heterogeneous.
- IGF2 overexpression is a key feature of sporadic BWS.
- Multiple mechanisms of loss of IGF2 imprinting have been identified in BWS.
- Mutations affecting the p57^{KIP2} (CDKN1C) gene account for a minority of cases of BWS overall, but are an important cause in familial cases.
- Phenotypic overlap in BWS patients between those with IGF2 overexpression and those with p57^{KIP2} mutations suggests that the mutations affect different parts of a common growth control pathway.
- Elucidating the mechanisms and consequences of imprinting, the function of the H19 gene, and the precise roles of p57^{KIP2} and IGF2 defects in BWS are among the many exciting future challenges in this field.

References

Brown KW, Villar AJ, Bickmore W *et al.* 1996 Imprinting mutation in the Beckwith-Wiedemann syndrome leads to biallelic IGF2 expression through an H19 independent pathway. *Human Molecular Genetics* **6** 2027–2032.

Catchpoole D, Lam WWK, Valler D *et al.* 1997 Epigenetic modification and uniparental inheritance of H19 in Beckwith-Wiedemann Syndrome. *Journal of Medical Genetics* **34** 353–359.

Elliott M & Maher ER 1994 Syndrome of the month: Beckwith-Wiedemann syndrome. *Journal of Medical Genetics* **31** 560–564.

Hatada I, Ohashi H, Fukushima Y *et al.* 1996 An imprinted gene p57^{KIP2} is mutated in Beckwith-Wiedemann syndrome. *Nature Genetics* **14** 171–173.

Hatada I, Nabetani A, Morisaki H *et al.* 1997 New p57^{KIP2} mutations in Beckwith-Wiedemann syndrome. *Human Genetics* **100** 681–683.

Henri I, Bonaiti-Pellie C, Chehensse V *et al.* 1991 Uniparental paternal disomy in a genetic cancer-predisposing syndrome. *Nature* **351** 665–667.

Joyce JA, Lam WWK, Catchpoole DJ *et al.* 1997 Imprinting of IGF2 and H19: lack of reciprocity in sporadic Beckwith-Wiedemann Syndrome. *Human Molecular Genetics* **6** 1543–1548.

Lam WWK, Hatada I, Mukai T, Joyce JA, Cole TRP, Donnai D, Reik W, Schofield PN & Maher ER 1999 Analysis of germline *CDKN1C (p57^{KIP2})* mutations in familial and sporadic Beckwith-Wiedemann syndrome (BWS) provides a novel genotype-phenotype correlation. *Journal of Medical Genetics.*

Lee MP, Debaun M, Randhawa G, Reichard BA, Elledge SJ & Feinberg AP 1997*a* Low frequency of p57^{KIP2} mutation in Beckwith-Wiedemann syndrome. *American Journal of Genetics* **61** 304–309.

Lee MP, Hu RJ, Johnson LA & Feinberg AP 1997*b* Human KVLQT1 gene shows tissue specific imprinting and encompasses Beckwith-Wiedemann syndrome chromosomal rearrangements. *Nature Genetics* **15** 181–185.

Leighton PA, Ingrams RS, Eggenschwiler J, Efstratiadis A & Tilghman SM 1995 Disruption of imprinting caused by deletion of theH19 gene region in mice. *Nature* **375** 34–39.

O'Keefe D, Dao D, Zhao L *et al.* 1997 Coding mutations in p57^{KIP2} are present in some cases of Beckwith-Wiedemann Syndrome but are rare or absent in Wilms' tumor. *American Journal of Human Genetics* **61** 295–303.

Okamoto K, Morison IM, Reeve AE, Tommerup N, Wiedemann HR & Friedrich U 1998 Is p57KIP2 mutation a common mechanism for Beckwith-Wiedemann syndrome or somatic overgrowth? *Journal of Medical Genetics* **35** 86.

Reik W, Brown K, Schneid H, Le Bouc Y, Bickmore W & Maher ER 1995 Imprinting mutations in Beckwith-Wiedemann syndrome suggested by an altered imprinting pattern in the IGF2-H19 domain. *Human Molecular Genetics* **4** 2379–2385.

Reik W & Maher ER 1997 Imprinting in clusters: lessons from Beckwith-Wiedemann Syndrome. *Trends in Genetics* **3** 330–334.

Slatter RE, Elliott M, Welham K, Carrera M, Schofield PN, Barton DE & Maher ER 1994 Mosaic uniparental disomy in Beckwith–Weidemann syndrome. *Journal of Medical Genetics* **31** 749–753.

Smilinich NJ, Day CD, Fitzpatrick GV, Caldwell GM, Lossie AC, Cooper PR, Smallwood AC, Joyce JA, Schofield PN, Reik W, Nicholls RD, Driscoll DJ, Maher ER, Shows TB & Higgins MJ in press A maternally methylated CpG-island in *KvLQT1* is associated with an antisense paternal transcript and loss of imprinting in Beckwith–Weidemann syndrome. *Proceedings of the National Academy of Sciences of the USA.*

Sun FL, Dean WL, Kelsey G, Allen ND & Reik W 1997 Transactivation of Igf2 in a mouse model of Beckwith-Wiedemann Syndrome. *Nature* **389** 809–815.

Weksberg R, Shen DR, Fei YL, Song QL & Squire J 1993 Disruption of insulin-like growth factor imprinting in Beckwith-Wiedemann Syndrome. *Nature Genetics* **5** 143–150.

Zhang P, Liegois NJ, Wong C *et al.* 1997 Altered cell differentiation and proliferation in mice lacking p57KIP2 indicates a role in Beckwith-Wiedemann syndrome. *Nature* **387** 151–158.

Genetic Insights in Paediatric Endocrinology and Metabolism
Eds S O'Rahilly and D B Dunger
BioScientifica Ltd, Bristol (1999)

Determinants of normal variation in size at birth

K Woods

University Department of Paediatrics, John Radcliffe Hospital,
Oxford OX4 1PB, UK

We have known for some time that low birthweight increases the risk of perinatal and infant mortality and morbidity. More recently, however, epidemiological studies by Barker and others have demonstrated a clear association between small size at birth and an increased risk of diseases prevalent amongst the adult population of developed countries, cardiovascular disease and type 2 diabetes (Barker 1994, Phillips 1996). It is important to note that these intriguing associations are *continuous* across the spectrum of birthweights: in most studies, the higher the birthweight, the lower the risk. The mechanism(s) which underlie(s) these associations remain controversial. This chapter focuses on the current state of knowledge of the genetic factors involved in fetal somatic growth, and discusses the evidence that these may be involved in the origins of adult disease.

Determinants of size at birth

We can postulate that primary growth potential of a fetus is determined by the functioning of his/her fetal growth genes. Environmental factors acting on the fetus *in utero* may then modulate fetal growth. These 'fetal environmental' factors include maternal factors (such as nutrition, smoking, disease and uterine size), fetal non-genetic factors, (such as fetal disease) and placental function, the placenta having an essential role in partitioning nutrient between fetus and mother.

It has been suggested that these environmental factors, in particular delivery of nutrient to the fetus, routinely limit fetal growth potential and that, as a consequence, fetal genes are of little importance for determining size at birth in the majority of babies (Phillips 1996). Barker and others have thus proposed that the link between reduced fetal growth and adult disease can be explained by environmental mechanisms only: hypothesising that fetal undernutrition results in a permanent metabolic adaptation, or 'programming' of fetal metabolism, ultimately leading to adult disease (Hales *et al.* 1991, Barker 1995). In the case of type 2 diabetes, they hypothesise that fetal undernutrition leads both to reduced β-cell mass and insulin resistance (Phillips 1996).

Alternatively, genes, or 'genotypes', which reduce size at birth may also confer an increased risk of adult disease. As discussed below, in addition to having a direct effect on fetal growth, the fetal genome also affects placental function, thus providing a mechanism whereby genetics may determine fetal nutrient supply.

It is possible that such adverse genotypes may have conferred a survival advantage throughout most of human evolution but that, in our present affluent society, are disadvantageous. In 1962, Neel put forward a similar hypothesis to explain the rising incidence of type 2 diabetes (Neel 1962). He suggested that a genetic make-up which allows tolerance of cyclic changes in food availability (as would be the case in the hunter/gatherer society) may be detrimental in conditions of more plentiful food supply, leading to metabolic decompensation, either directly or through a tendency to obesity.

Genetic influences on fetal growth

The insulin-like growth factors IGF-I and IGF-II have crucial roles in fetal growth. They and the type 1 and type 2 IGF receptors are also extensively discussed in the chapters by O'Rahilly and Maher.

IGF-II gene (IGF2) and IGF-I gene (IGF1) knockout mouse models

Both the murine and the human IGF-II genes (*IGF2*) are imprinted, with sole expression from the paternal allele (Barlow *et al.* 1991, Giannuokakis *et al.* 1993). Targeted disruption of the paternal *IGF2* allele in the mouse reduced embryonic and placental growth, with divergence of growth noticeable from embryonic day (ed) 10.5 until term, resulting in birthweight 60% of normal (DeChiara *et al.* 1990). Postnatal growth was unaffected, although no 'catch-up' growth occurred, suggesting the growth-promoting effects of IGF-II in the mouse are limited to fetal life.

Homozygous disruption of the murine IGF-I gene (*IGF1*) also produces growth failure from ed 13.5 until term, birthweight again being reduced to 60% of control birthweight (Liu *et al.* 1993, Baker *et al.* 1993, Powell-Braxton *et al.* 1993). Placental growth was unaffected. A significant proportion (up to 95%, dependent on genetic strain) of the homozygous mutants died at birth, apparently of respiratory failure. Postnatal growth was also affected, the surviving mice being 30% the size of controls.

Mediation of IGF-I and IGF-II effects

The type 1 IGF receptor (or IGF-I receptor) is a heterotetrameric protein, homologous to the insulin receptor. It binds IGF-I with high affinity, and IGF-II with lesser affinity. Homozygous knockout of the IGF-I receptor gene (*IGF1R*) produced a more severe phenotype than either *IGF1* or *IGF2* knockouts, with birthweight of the homozygous mutants 45% of normal, and 100% neonatal lethality (Liu *et al.* 1993, Baker *et al.* 1993). Additional disruption of *IGF1* did not affect the phenotype, suggesting that all the growth-promoting effects of IGF-I are mediated through the IGF-I receptor. The addition of an *IGF2* null allele, however, resulted in a further reduction of embryonic growth, suggesting that some of the growth-promoting effects of IGF-II are mediated through another receptor (Baker *et al.* 1993). More recently, this has been demonstrated to be the insulin receptor (Louvi *et al.* 1997).

IGF-II can bind to yet another receptor, the type 2 IGF receptor. This receptor, structurally unrelated to the insulin receptor family, is bifunctional, also acting as a receptor for mannose 6-phosphate, which is involved in the trafficking of lysosomal enzymes. Like *IGF2*, murine *IGF2R* is imprinted but, in this case, is expressed from the *maternal*, rather than the paternal, allele (Kalscheuer *et al.* 1993). In humans, however, *IGF2R* is not imprinted.

Knockout of *IGF2R* in the mouse produced the rather surprising phenotype of embryonic overgrowth from ed 13.5, with birthweight 35% above normal (Wang *et al.* 1994, Lau *et al.* 1994).

In addition, the mutant mice had polydactyly, cardiac anomalies and almost complete neonatal lethality. IGF-II levels were increased 4-fold, suggesting that this receptor, rather than mediating a growth-promoting effect of IGF-II, has a role in limiting IGF-II levels in the circulation, which otherwise overstimulate the IGF-I receptor, resulting in overgrowth. Introduction of either an *IGF2* or an *IGF1R* null allele rescued the phenotype.

IGFs in human fetal growth

The knockout experiments described above have given us a clear idea of the role of the IGFs and their receptors in mouse embryonic growth. Although these studies might shed some light on the role of IGFs in man, it is unlikely that the functioning of the IGF system in man will be identical to that in the mouse. In man, we are more reliant on 'experiments of nature' to provide us with further information.

Human IGF1 deletion

A recent discovery of a child with a homozygous partial deletion of *IGF1* has confirmed the important role of IGF-I in human growth, both before and after birth (Woods *et al.* 1996). The patient was severely growth-retarded at birth (1.3 kg at 37 weeks' gestation) and, by the age of 15.5 years, his height standard deviation score (SDS) was –6.7. Other problems included sensorineural deafness and mild mental retardation, suggesting that IGF-I may play a part in human neurological development.

Interestingly, this patient had significant insulin resistance, which improved once he was treated with recombinant human IGF-I (rhIGF-I). Before therapy was started, growth hormone (GH) levels were extremely high in this child, and we hypothesise that the insulin resistance was secondary to the direct, 'anti-insulin'-like effect of GH. rhIGF-I normalised GH secretion, thus improving insulin sensitivity (Woods *et al.* 1997, Camacho-Hübner *et al.* 1999). This patient thus provides an example of a genetic mechanism linking reduced fetal growth and insulin resistance.

IGF-I and normal variation in birthweight

Apart from this single case, considerable indirect evidence exists that variation in IGF-I levels play a part in the normal variation in human birthweight. A number of studies have now demonstrated a positive association between IGF-I levels and both fetal size (Lassarre *et al.* 1991, Giudice *et al.* 1995, Leger *et al.* 1996), and size at birth (Langford *et al.* 1994, Varvarigou *et al.* 1994, Leger *et al.* 1995, Ogilvy Stuart *et al.* 1998). IGF-I levels, both before and after birth, are nutritionally responsive, possibly via insulin secretion (see below). In animal studies, infusion of IGF-I into the fetus has been shown to enhance placental amino-acid and glucose uptake, suggesting that IGF-I may regulate fetal growth in relationship to fetal nutrient supply (Harding *et al.* 1994).

IGF-II and human fetal growth

No human case of an *IGF2* mutation has yet been described. However, there is some evidence that human overgrowth syndromes such as the Beckwith–Wiedemann syndrome are associated with *IGF2* overexpression (see the chapter by Maher). These cases suggest that *IGF2* does play some part in human fetal growth: the importance of this role remains to be determined. Unlike IGF-I, levels of IGF-II do not correlate with size at birth: this, however, does not rule out a role for IGF-II in earlier fetal growth.

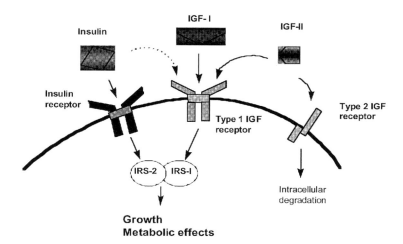

Figure 1 Model of IGF and insulin receptor interactions based on targeted gene disruption studies. Insulin signals mainly through the insulin receptor, but can also utilise the type 1 IGF receptor, albeit with lesser affinity. The growth-promoting effects of IGF-I are mediated through the type 1 IGF receptor. IGF-II also utilises the type 1 IGF receptor, and, to a lesser extent the insulin receptor (not shown) to exert its growth-promoting effects. The type 2 IGF receptor, structurally very different from the other two receptors, targets IGF-II for degradation. The insulin and type 1 IGF receptors utilise the same intracellular signalling pathway, the first step of which is activation of insulin receptor substrates (IRS) 1 and 2.

Insulin and fetal growth

Insulin, produced in the fetal pancreas from early in gestation, has both direct and indirect effects on the growth of the fetus. Insulin enhances the uptake of glucose into cells and has direct anabolic effects, mainly on cell turnover rather than differentiation (Fowden 1995). In addition, insulin stimulates IGF-I transcription, and regulates IGF-I bio-availability through its effect on IGF binding proteins such as IGF binding protein-1 (Gluckman & Harding 1997). In fetal life, GH has little effect on IGF-I levels, and thus insulin may be the prime regulator of IGF-I production, providing a mechanism whereby fetal growth is highly nutritionally sensitive.

Genetic studies of insulin and fetal growth

In the mouse, targeted disruption of genes involved in pancreatic development, and hence insulin production (such as the pancreatic transcription factor insulin promoter factor-1: IPF-1), produces severe

125

growth retardation *in utero*, in addition to early postnatal death from ketoacidosis (Jonsson *et al.* 1994). In man, IPF-1 gene mutations, associated with pancreatic agenesis, are also associated with severe insulin deficiency and severe prenatal growth failure (Stoffers *et al.* 1997).

Surprisingly, however, homozygous insulin receptor knockout mice do not exhibit growth retardation, although they uniformly die in the neonatal period from ketoacidosis (Joshi *et al.* 1996). It is thought that the normal prenatal growth in these mice may be due to insulin signalling through the IGF-I receptor, to which it can bind, albeit at lower affinity. In man, severe disruption of the insulin receptor gene has been reported in leprechaunism, a condition associated with severe growth retardation at birth (Psiachou *et al.* 1993, Wertheimer *et al.* 1993, Krook & O'Rahilly 1996), suggesting that insulin signalling through the IGF-I receptor is not sufficient to preserve human fetal growth.

Figure 1 summarises the complex interactions between insulin, the IGFs and their receptors. As has been discussed, the homology between these growth factors and their receptors allows this system to be highly 'promiscuous', growth factors having the opportunity to signal through more than one receptor.

At the post-receptor level, the insulin and IGF-I receptor also utilise the same intracellular signalling pathway, with the first stage being activation of the insulin receptor substrates 1 and 2 (IRS-1 and IRS-2). Targeted disruption of either the IRS-1 and IRS-2 genes produces embryonic growth failure, perhaps not surprising given their common utilisation by insulin and IGF-I. In addition, the knockout mice had insulin resistance, more severe in the IRS-2 gene than the IRS-1 gene knockout (Tamemoto *et al.* 1994, Withers *et al.* 1998). In man, polymorphisms of IRS-1 have been associated, in some studies, with insulin resistance and type 2 diabetes (Almind *et al.* 1993, Laakso *et al.* 1994, Imai *et al.* 1994, Clausen *et al.* 1995, Hitman *et al.* 1995, Zhang *et al.* 1996). Potentially, genetic variations in the functioning of IRS-1, IRS-2 or other intracellular molecules involved in the insulin/IGF-I signalling pathway may produce more subtle variations in growth *in utero* and insulin resistance.

Glucokinase gene mutations

The pancreatic β-cell is highly sensitive to circulating glucose concentrations, in order to secrete insulin at the appropriate level to maintain normoglycaemia. The activity of glucokinase (GK), the enzyme which catalyses the conversion of glucose to glucose 6-phosphate in the β-cell, appears to be the rate-limiting step in the uptake of glucose into the cell, thus controlling the level of glucose at which insulin is secreted (Grupe *et al.* 1995). In man, heterozygous GK gene mutations have been associated with one form of maturity onset diabetes of the young (MODY) (Hattersley 1998). Patients possessing the mutation have mild hyperglycaemia and hyperinsulinaemia, presumably due to an altered 'set-point' between glucose levels, and insulin secretion.

As discussed in the chapter by Hattersley, he and his co-workers have recently published an elegant study associating the presence or absence of a GK gene mutation with variation in birthweight (Hattersley *et al.* 1998). Sib pairs discordant for possession of a GK gene mutation were compared. *In utero*, the glucose levels of the fetus are determined by maternal glucose concentration, and it was therefore proposed that the fetus with a GK gene mutation would secrete less insulin, and hence be smaller, than the fetus with no mutation. This was indeed the case, birthweight being reduced by just over 0.5 kg on average in those with the mutation. Conversely, the offspring of mothers who possessed the mutation themselves were just over 0.5 kg heavier, presumably as a consequence of mild fetal hyper-insulinaemia. This study demonstrates that relatively mild genetically determined variations in insulin production can affect human fetal growth.

Birthweight effects of the insulin gene VNTR polymorphism

GK gene mutations remain a very rare cause of insulin deficiency. What evidence is there that more prevalent genetic polymorphisms affect the normal variation in size at birth? As described in the chapter by Todd, the insulin gene (*INS*) variable number of tandem repeats (VNTR) is a polymorphism located within the promoter region of *INS*. This polymorphism has tissue-specific transcriptional effects on both *INS* and *IGF2* (which is contiguous to *INS*). I and III are the two main allele classes of *INS* VNTR: in the Caucasian population, 47% are class I homozygotes, 9% class III homozygotes and 43% I/II heterozygotes. The type I allele has been associated in a number of studies with type 1 diabetes, and the type III allele has shown a weaker association with type 2 diabetes.

We recently studied the effect of *INS* VNTR genotype on size at birth (Dunger *et al.* 1998). *INS* VNTR genotype (using the closely linked –23 *HphI* polymorphism) was determined in 758 normal term singleton neonates, born in the English County of Avon (the ALSPAC Children in Focus [CIF] cohort). Detailed growth data at birth and 2 years was available for each child. Weight, length and head circumference were all greater in class III homozygotes (III/IIIs), when compared with class I homozygotes (I/Is) or heterozygotes (III/IIIs). When the cohort was studied as a whole, however, this difference was only significant for head circumference (I/I 34.81 cm vs III/III 35.42 cm, P = 0.004; I/I vs I/III vs III/III, P = 0.008).

In the ALSPAC CIF cohort, 55% of the infants showed a change in weight SDS score larger than 0.67 SD over the first 2 years of life, equivalent to moving up or down one 'centile band' on standard growth charts, and indicative of significant 'catch-up' or 'catch-down' growth. In these 55% (changers), factors related to the maternal uterine environment, such as mother's pre-pregnancy weight, pregnancy weight gain, parity and smoking, were important in determining variance in birthweight (combined r^2 = 23.4%). Furthermore, the correlation coefficient between birth length and mid-parental height (an estimate of genetic height potential) was poor at birth ($r = 0.26$), but improved by two years ($r = 0.44$). In contrast, in the remaining 45% (non-changers), maternal uterine factors had a lesser effect on birthweight (combined r^2 = 12.4%) and correlations between birth length and mid-parental height were higher at birth ($r = 0.39$) and similar at 2 years ($r = 0.42$).

Thus, these analyses of postnatal growth identified babies (the 45% non-changers) in whom the genetic contribution to variation in size at birth (i.e. the effect of the *INS* VNTR) was amplified and was less confounded by maternal uterine factors. In addition to head circumference (I/I 34.79 cm vs III/III 35.69 cm, *P* = 0.0005), length (I/I 50.68 cm vs III/III 51.95 cm, *P* = 0.015) and weight (I/I 3434 g vs III/III 3692 g, *P* = 0.0005) were also significantly higher in III/IIIs.

Cord blood hormone levels were analysed in a subset (77 non-changers) of the ALSPAC CIF cohort in whom samples were available. III/IIIs had higher levels of insulin, IGF-II, and IGF-I than either I/Is and I/IIIs, the differences reaching significance for IGF-II and IGF-I (Table 1).

Table 1 Correlation of cord blood hormone levels and *INS* VNTR genotype among 77 non-changers in the ALSPAC CIF cohort

	Genotype			ANOVA I/I vs III/III
	I/I (*n* = 39)	I/III (n = 33)	III/III (*n* = 5)	
Insulin (pmol/l)	3.09	2.78	5.12	P = 0.08
IGF-I (nmol/l)	296.9	281.7	390.7	P = 0.02
IGF-II (nmol/l)	88.2	93.0	128.1	P = 0.01

Summary and conclusions

Human fetal growth involves a complex interaction between environment and genes. The genes encoding insulin and the IGFs, their receptors and intracellular signalling molecules are central to both fetal growth and to determination of insulin secretion and sensitivity. Thus, common polymorphisms within these genes are strong candidates in the search to explain the associations between fetal growth, insulin resistance and adult disease. As our study into the effects of the *INS* VNTR on size at birth demonstrates, however, careful follow-up of the growth of birth cohorts helps to dissect out the influences of genes and environment.

References

Almind K, Bjorbaek C, Vestergaard H, Hansen T, Echwald S & Pedersen O 1993 Aminoacid polymorphisms of insulin receptor substrate-1 in non- insulin-dependent diabetes mellitus. *Lancet* **342** 828–832.

Baker J, Liu J, Robertson EJ & Efstratiadis A 1993 Role of insulin-like growth factors in embryonic and postnatal growth. *Cell* **75** 73–82.

Barker DJ 1994 *Mothers, Babies, and Diseases in Later Life.* London:BMT publishing group.

Barker DJ 1995 Fetal origins of coronary heart disease. *British Medical Journal* **311** 171–174.

Barlow DP, Stoger R, Herrmann BG, Salto K & Schweifer N 1991 The mouse insulin-like growth factor type-2 receptor is imprinted and closely linked to the Tme locus. *Nature* **349** 84–87.

Camacho-Hübner C, Woods KA, Miraki-Moud F, Hindmarsh PC, Clark AJL, Hansson Y, Johnston A, Baxter RC & Savage MO 1999 Effects of recombinant human insulin-like growth factor (IGF)-I therapy on the growth hormone (GH)-IGF system of a patient with a partial IGF-I gene deletion. *Journal of Clinical Endocrinology and Metabolism* **84** 1611–1616.

Clausen JO, Hansen T, Bjorbaek C, Echwald SM, Urhammer SA, Rasmussen S, Andersen CB, Hansen L, Almind K, Winther K *et al.* 1995 Insulin resistance: interactions between obesity and a common variant of insulin receptor substrate-1. *Lancet* **346** 397–402.

DeChiara TM, Efstratiadis A & Robertson EJ 1990 A growth-deficiency phenotype in heterozygous mice carrying an insulin-like growth factor II gene disrupted by targeting. *Nature* **345** 78–80.

Dunger DB, Ong KKL, Huxtable S, Sherriff A, Woods KA, Ahmed ML, Golding J, Pembrey ME, Ring S, the ALSPAC study team, Bennett ST & Todd JA 1998 Association of the INS VNTR with size at birth. *Nature Genetics* **19** 98–100.

Fowden AL 1995 Endocrine regulation of fetal growth. *Reproduction, Fertility and Development* **7** 351–363.

Giannoukakis N, Deal C, Paquette J, Goodyer CG & Polychronakos C 1993 Parental genomic imprinting of the human IGF2 gene. *Nature Genetics* **4** 98–101.

Giudice LC, de Zegher F, Gargosky SE, Dsupin BA, de las Fuentes L, Crystal RA, Hintz RL & Rosenfeld RG 1995 Insulin-like growth factors and their binding proteins in the term and preterm human fetus and neonate with normal and extremes of intrauterine growth. *Journal of Clinical Endocrinology and Metabolism* **80** 1548–1555.

Gluckman PD & Harding JE 1997 The physiology and pathophysiology of intrauterine growth retardation. *Hormone Research* **48** suppl. 1 11–16.

Grupe A, Hultgren B, Ryan A, Ma YH, Bauer M & Stewart TA 1995. Transgenic knockouts reveal a critical requirement for pancreatic beta cell glucokinase in maintaining glucose homeostasis. *Cell* **83** 69–78.

Hales CN, Barker DJ, Clark PM, Cox LJ, Fall C, Osmond C & Winter PD 1991 Fetal and infant growth and impaired glucose tolerance at age 64. *British Medical Journal* **303** 1019–1022.

Harding JE, Liu L, Evans PC & Gluckman PD 1994 Insulin-like growth factor 1 alters feto-placental protein and carbohydrate metabolism in fetal sheep. *Endocrinology* **134** 1509–1514.

Hattersley AT 1998 Maturity-onset diabetes of the young: clinical heterogeneity explained by genetic heterogeneity (published erratum appears in *Diabetic Medicine* 1998 **15** 437). *Diabetic Medicine* **15** 15–24.

Hattersley AT, Beards F, Ballantyne E, Appleton M, Harvey R & Ellard S 1998 Mutations in the glucokinase gene of the fetus result in reduced birthweight (see comments). *Nature Genetics* **19** 268–270.

Hitman GA, Hawrami K, McCarthy MI, Viswanathan M, Snehalatha C, Ramachandran A, Tuomilehto J, Tuomilehto Wolf E, Nissinen A & Pedersen O 1995 Insulin receptor substrate-1 gene mutations in NIDDM; implications for the study of polygenic disease. *Diabetologia* **38** 481–486.

Imai, Y, Fusco A, Suzuki Y, Lesniak MA, D'Alfonso R, Sesti G, Bertoli A, Lauro R, Accili D & Taylor SI 1994 Variant sequences of insulin receptor substrate-1 in patients with noninsulin-dependent diabetes mellitus. *Journal of Clinical Endocrinology and Metabolism* **79** 1655–1658.

Jonsson J, Carlsson L, Edlund T & Edlund H 1994 Insulin-promoter-factor 1 is required for pancreas development in mice. *Nature* **371** 606–609.

Joshi RL, Lamothe B, Cordonnier N, Mesbah K, Monthioux E, Jami J & Bucchini D 1996 Targeted disruption of the insulin receptor gene in the mouse results in neonatal lethality. *EMBO Journal* **15** 1542–1547.

Kalscheuer VM, Mariman EC, Schepens MT, Rehder H & Ropers HH 1993 The insulin-like growth factor type-2 receptor gene is imprinted in mouse but not in humans. *Nature Genetics* **5** 79–82.

Krook A & O'Rahilly S 1996 Mutant insulin receptors in syndromes of insulin resistance. *Baillieres Clinical Endocrinology and Metabolism* **10** 97–122.

Laakso M, Malkki M, Kekalainen P, Kuusisto J & Deeb SS 1994 Insulin receptor substrate-1 variants in non-insulin-dependent diabetes. *Journal of Clinical Investigation* **94** 1141–1146.

Langford K, Blum W, Nicolaides K, Jones J, McGregor A & Miell J 1994 The pathophysiology of the insulin-like growth factor axis in fetal growth failure: a basis for programming by undernutrition? *European Journal of Clinical Investigation* **24** 851–856.

Lassarre C, Hardouin S, Daffos F, Forestier F, Frankenne F & Binoux M 1991 Serum insulin-like growth factors and insulin-like growth factor binding proteins in the human fetus. Relationships with growth in normal subjects and in subjects with intrauterine growth retardation. *Pediatric Research* **29** 219–225.

Lau MM, Stewart CE, Liu Z, Bhatt H, Rotwein P & Stewart CL 1994 Loss of imprinted IGF2/ cation-independent mannose 6-phosphate receptor results in fetal overgrowth and perinatal lethality. *Genes and Development* **8** 2953–2963.

Leger J, Oury JF, Noel M, Baron S, Benali K, Blot P & Czernichow P 1996 Growth factors and intrauterine growth retardation. I. Serum growth hormone, insulin-like growth factor (IGF)-I, IGF-II, and IGF binding protein 3 levels in normally grown and growth-retarded human fetuses during the second half of gestation. *Pediatric Research* **40** 94–100.

Leger J, Noel M, Limal JM, Czernichow P on behalf of the Study Group of IUGR 1995 Growth factors and intrauterine growth retardation. II. Serum growth hormone, insulin-like growth factor (IGF)-I, and IGF-binding protein 3 levels in children with intrauterine growth retardation as compared with normal controls: prospective study from birth to two years of age. *Pediatric Research* **40** 101–107.

Liu J, Baker J, Perkins AS, Robertson EJ & Efstratiadis A 1993 Mice carrying null mutations of the genes encoding insulin-like growth factor I (*Igf-1*) and type 1 IGF receptor (*Igf1r*). *Cell* **75** 59–72.

Louvi A, Accili D & Efstratiadis A 1997 Growth-promoting interaction of IGF-II with the insulin receptor during mouse embryonic development. *Developmental Biology* **189** 33–48.

Neel JV 1962 Diabetes mellitus: a thrifty genotype rendered detrimental by 'progress'? *American Journal of Human Genetics* **14** 353–362.

Ogilvy Stuart AL, Hands SJ, Adcock CJ, Holly JM, Matthews DR, Mohamed Ali V, Yudkin JS, Wilkinson AR & Dunger DB 1998 Insulin, insulin-like growth factor I (IGF-I), IGF-binding protein-1, growth hormone, and feeding in the newborn. *Journal of Clinical Endocrinology and Metabolism* **83** 3550–3557.

Phillips, DIW 1996 Insulin resistance as a programmed response to fetal undernutrition. *Diabetol* **39** 1119–1122.

Powell-Braxton L, Hollinghead P, Warburton C, Dowd M, Pitts-Meek S, Dalton D, Gillett N & Stewart TA 1993 IGF-I is required for normal embryonic growth in mice. *Genes and Development* **7** 2609–2617.

Psiachou H, Mitton S, Alaghband Zadeh J, Hone J, Taylor SI & Sinclair L 1993 Leprechaunism and homozygous nonsense mutation in the insulin receptor gene. *Lancet* **342** 924.

Stoffers DA, Zinkin NT, Stanojevic V, Clarke WL & Habener JF 1997 Pancreatic agenesis attributable to a single nucleotide deletion in the human IPF1 gene coding sequence. *Nature Genetics* **15** 106–110.

Tamemoto H, Kadowaki T, Tobe K, Yagi T, Sakura H, Hayakawa T, Terauchi Y, Ueki K, Kaburagi Y, Satoh S *et al.* 1994 Insulin resistance and growth retardation in mice lacking insulin receptor substrate-1. *Nature* **372** 182–186.

Varvarigou A, Vagenakis AG, Makri M & Beratis NG 1994 Growth hormone, insulin-like growth factor-I and prolactin in small for gestational age neonates. *Biology of the Neonate* **65** 94–102.

Wang ZQ, Fung MR, Barlow DP & Wagner EF 1994 Regulation of embryonic growth and lysosomal targeting by the imprinted Igf2/Mpr gene. *Nature* **372** 464–467.

Wertheimer E, Lu SP, Backeljauw PF, Davenport ML & Taylor SI 1993 Homozygous deletion of the human insulin receptor gene results in leprechaunism. *Nature Genetics* **5** 71–73.

Withers DJ, Gutierrez JS, Towery H, Burks DJ, Ren JM, Previs S, Zhang Y, Bernal D, Pons S, Shulman GI, Bonner Weir S & White MF 1998 Disruption of IRS-2 causes type 2 diabetes in mice. *Nature* **391** 900–904.

Woods KA, Camacho-Hübner C, Barter D, Clark AJL & Savage MO 1997 Insulin-like growth factor I gene deletion causing intrauterine growth retardation and severe short stature. *Acta Paediatrica Supplement* **423** 39–45.

Woods KA, Camacho-Hübner C, Savage MO & Clark AJL 1996 Intrauterine growth retardation and postnatal growth failure associated with deletion of the insulin-like growth factor I gene. *New England Journal of Medicine* **335** 1363–1367.

Zhang Y, Wat N, Stratton IM, Warren Perry MG, Orho M, Groop L & Turner RC 1996 UKPDS 19: heterogeneity in NIDDM: separate contributions of IRS-1 and beta 3-adrenergic-receptor mutations to insulin resistance and obesity respectively with no evidence for glycogen synthase gene mutations. UK Prospective Diabetes Study. *Diabetologia* **39** 1505–1511.

Bone mineral metabolism in growth hormone deficiency

G Saggese and G I Baroncelli

Endocrine Unit, Division of Pediatrics, Department of Reproductive Medicine
and Pediatrics, University of Pisa, Pisa, Italy

Increasing evidence suggests that growth hormone (GH), in addition to its
effect on linear growth, may play an important role in bone mineral
metabolism. This paper focuses on three main aspects of GH activity: the
physiological action of GH on bone metabolism; the effects of GH
deficiency on bone turnover and bone mineral density (BMD); and the
benefits of GH therapy on these parameters.

The physiological action of GH on bone metabolism

GH and bone metabolism

It is thought that GH acts on bone by a dual mechanism: a direct effect on
growth plate chondrocytes, and an indirect action by way of IGF-I. GH
determines the differentiation of chondrocyte precursors and the local
production of and responsiveness to IGF-I, which in turn mediates the local
clonal expansion of chondrocytes. GH directly stimulates osteoblasts,
leading to increased mineralisation and synthesis of bone matrix. The effect
of GH on osteoclasts is less clear; it may be direct, or mediated by factors
such as parathyroid hormone (PTH) or interleukin 6 (IL-6). Acting together,
these effects bring about longitudinal growth of bone, skeletal mineral
maturation and bone mineralisation.

GH also influences bone metabolism by its action on other target organs,
mainly the kidney and intestine. In the kidney, GH stimulates renal tubular
absorption of phosphate, resulting in decreased phosphaturia and increased
serum phosphate levels; it also increases TMP/GFR (maximum rate of renal
tubular phosphate absorption normalised to the glomerular filtration rate)
and consequently the production of 1,25-dihydroxy-vitamin D.

This in turn stimulates intestinal absorption of calcium and phosphate.
GH may also directly increase intestinal sensitivity to 1,25-dihydroxy
vitamin D. In combination, these effects raise the calcium × phosphate
product in the extracellular fluid, which appears to be the main mechanism

leading to optimum bone mineralisation during adolescence (Saggese *et al.* 1995).

GH and bone mass

Bone mass increases during childhood, reaches its peak in late adolescence, enters a plateau phase and decreases in later life, particularly in women after the menopause. Peak bone mass (PBM) can be defined as the highest bone mass achieved during life as a result of normal growth. An optimum PBM, as modified by age-related bone loss, is the major factor determining individual bone mass; attaining optimum PBM is the best way of preventing osteoporosis and minimising susceptibility to fractures (Bonjour *et al.* 1997, Matkovic *et al.* 1994).

Effects of GHD on bone

Bone turnover

GHD has profound effects on bone turnover, bone metabolism and BMD. In one series of 26 children with GHD whose mean chronological age was 8.3 ± 2.5 years, mean serum levels of the bone metabolism markers osteocalcin (6.0 ± 3.9 µg/l) and carboxy-terminal propeptide of type I procollagen (PICP) (181.6 ± 22.4 µg/l) were significantly ($P < 0.001$) below normal ranges (7–18 µg/l, 280–370 µg/l respectively), indicating reduced bone formation (Saggese *et al.* 1993). Osteocalcin is the most abundant non-collagenous bone protein produced by osteoblasts, and PICP is the only collagen present in bone. The level of 1,25-dihydroxy-vitamin D was also significantly reduced (64.7 ± 11.2 pmol/l vs 74–109 pmol/l; $P < 0.001$), probably reflecting under-stimulation by GH/IGF-I (Saggese *et al.* 1993). In further studies, we confirmed the reduced levels of osteocalcin and PICP, and also found lower levels of the carboxy-terminal telopeptide of type I procollagen (ICTP) (Saggese *et al.* 1996a). Thus both bone formation and bone resorption were diminished in children with GHD.

BMD

Studies on radial BMD ($n = 26$,) by single-photon absorptiometry (SPA) (Saggese *et al.* 1993) and lumbar BMD by dual energy X-ray absorptiometry (DEXA) ($n = 32$) (Saggese *et al.* 1996b) in children with GHD showed that both were significantly ($P < 0.001$) diminished compared with reference

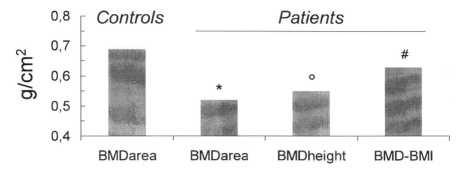

Figure 1 Children with GHD had significantly lower BMD than controls. Graph shows lumbar BMD, corrected for bone area, height and BMI (age 7.0 ± 0.7 years, *n* = 22). (Reproduced from Baroncelli *et al.* 1998 with permission.)

values, even when corrected for bone age. The distal radius is principally cortical bone, whereas the lumbar values gave an integrated measure of cortical and trabecular bone density. Because DEXA area results are influenced by several sources of variation, we recently corrected the lumbar area measurements for anthropometric variables, body height and BMI. As Fig. 1 shows, children with GHD had significantly lower BMD, corrected for bone area, body height and BMI, than controls. Lumbar BMD corrected for bone volume ($n = 22$) was also significantly lower in both boys ($P < 0,0005$) and girls ($P < 0.01$) than in controls (Baroncelli *et al.* 1998).

Effects of GH treatment on bone metabolism

Our own results from treating GDH children with recombinant human GH (rhGH) extend to over 6 years of follow-up, with a mean follow-up of 4 years. Children with a mean chronological age of 11.5 ± 2.3 years who were treated with rhGH showed a progressive increase in mean serum osteocalcin levels from around 10 ng/ml at baseline to a maximum of nearly 40 ng/ml at 12 months. Prepubertal patients received rhGH, 0.6 IU/kg per week in six subcutaneous doses; pubertal patients received 0.9 IU/kg per week in six subcutaneous doses (Saggese *et al.* 1996a).

Osteocalcin level declined thereafter, but was still above the normal range at 53–72 months. The increase from baseline was significant ($P < 0.001$) by the third month (Saggese *et al.* 1993). Levels of ICTP (the marker of bone resorption) and PICP rose, and remained elevated in a very similar manner (Saggese *et al.* 1996a). In addition, a highly significant positive correlation was seen between levels of PICP and osteocalcin as treatment progressed ($r = 0.41$, $P < 0.0001$). However, no correlation was evident between these two markers of bone formation and levels of ICTP (unpublished observations).

Several authors have reported correlations between the increase in levels of various bone markers and bone response to GH (Table 1). However, we found that the correlation between PICP levels and growth velocity disappeared after one year of rhGH treatment. In addition, follow-up of 11 patients showed no correlation between PICP levels and final height (unpublished observations).

Effects of rhGH treatment on BMD

Response of BMD to rhGH

Radial BMD measured by SPA and corrected for bone age increased steadily during treatment (Fig. 2). BMD was already significantly ($P < 0.01$) greater after one year than at baseline, and patients treated for the longest time – more than 6 years – achieved normal BMD values (Saggese *et al.* 1996b). Similar results were recorded for lumbar BMD (Saggese *et al.* 1996b) and lumbar BMD volume after two years' treatment (Boot *et al.* 1997).

Table 1 Predictive value of an increase in levels of various bone markers and bone response to GH

Bone marker, time	Growth velocity at	r	P	Reference
Osteocalcin, 3 months	12 months	–	<0.01	Johansen *et al.* 1990
PICP, 3 months	12 months	1.87	<0.001	Trivedi *et al.* 1991
Osteocalcin, 1 month	12 months	0.66	<0.01	Kanzaki *et al.* 1992
PICP, 1 week, 3 months	12 months	0.61	<0.001	Saggese *et al.* 1993
BAP, 3 months	12 months	1.67	<0.001	Crofton *et al.* 1995
Gal-Hyl 3 months	12 months	0.76	=0.002	Rauch *et al.* 1995
Pyr, 1 month	6 months	0.58	<0.05	Fujimoto *et al.* 1995
PICP, 1 month	12 months	0.68	<0.05	Kubo *et al.* 1995
Pyr, Dpd, 1 month	12 months	0.82	<0.05	Spagnoli *et al.* 1996

PICP, carboxy-terminal propeptide of type I procollagen; BAP, bone alkaline phosphatase isoenzyme; Gal-Hyl, galactosyl-hydroxylysine; Pyr, urinary; Dpd, urinary deoxypyridinoline.

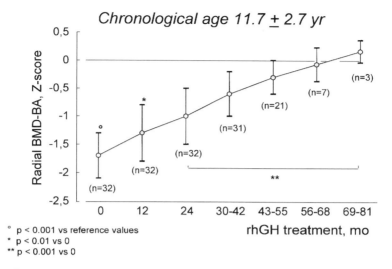

° p < 0.001 vs reference values
* p < 0.01 vs 0
** p < 0.001 vs 0

Figure 2 Radial BMD increased steadily in children with GHD during rhGH treatment. BMD was measured by single-photon absorptiometry (SPA) and corrected for bone age. (Reproduced from Saggese *et al.* 1996b with permission).

Optimal rhGH treatment, PBM and final height

In view of this positive effect of GH on bone mass, the question arises, 'why do young adults with childhood-onset GHD have lower bone mass if they have received treatment with GH?' (Saggese *et al.* 1995, Kaufman *et al.* 1992, De Boer *et al.* 1994). The main explanations for this effect seem to be: first, that patients did not reach PBM during treatment; secondly, they may have received GH treatment that was suboptimal with respect to dose, frequency of administration, and/or onset of treatment, as has been observed with human pituitary GH (PGH). A series of our early patients was evaluated at final height after initial non-optimal intramuscular treatment – in some beginning very late – with a low dose of PGH, 0.1 U/kg 2–3 times per week intermittently for 4 years, before rhGH therapy. Their lumbar BMD corrected for 'apparent' bone volume was significantly lower ($P < 0.04$) than those of a control group of children with familial short stature (Saggese *et al.* 1996b).

The decision to stop rhGH therapy is usually based on linear growth, and is taken when the growth velocity falls below 1–2 cm/year. Nevertheless, it has been shown that, during puberty, the increment in bone mass as a function of height increment follows a loop pattern in which the two variables become dissociated in late puberty; when the growth velocity abruptly decreases, bone mass continues to increase (Theintz *et al.* 1992). Consequently, GH therapy may often be discontinued before PBM has been attained. In addition, patients with GHD probably attain PBM later than unaffected children. Data on later incidence of fracture are sparse, but two papers have recently reported that the incidence of fracture in adults with GHD is increased (Wuster *et al.* 1991, Rosen *et al.* 1997)

Conclusions and the future

- Children with GHD show decreases in levels of biochemical markers of bone formation and resorption that suggest reduced bone turnover. They also have reduced BMD, even when values are corrected for bone age, BMI, body height and bone volume; these findings suggest that GHD itself affects the acquisition of bone mass.
- During treatment of GHD children with rhGH, serum levels of biochemical markers for bone formation and resorption are increased, suggesting increased bone turnover. In addition, levels of biochemical markers for bone formation are significantly correlated with each other, but not with levels of bone resorption markers.
- The increase of PICP can predict the short-term growth response to treatment, but not the long-term response or final height.
- After 2 years of GH treatment, radial and lumbar BMD increased significantly more from baseline than did height, and patients treated for longest showed normalisation of radial and lumbar BMD.
- Thus GH plays a specific role in the build-up of bone mass, and adequate GH treatment in childhood can restore BMD to normal at final height, whereas suboptimal treatment may result in subnormal BMD at final height.
- Some patients with GHD may not attain PBM even with 'adequate' GH treatment, because PBM is still to be achieved when final height is reached and GH therapy is discontinued.
- Children with GHD may take longer than unaffected children to reach PBM, because of growth failure.
- Finally, in the words of the recommendations of a recent consensus meeting on GH diagnosis and treatment, 'Adequate GH replacement therapy should be performed during childhood and adolescence, starting as early as possible and optimising treatment with respect to dosage to achieve normal BMD at the time of reaching final height. Consideration should be given to continuing GH therapy until PBM is achieved, despite final height having been attained.' (Saggese *et al.* 1998).

- Future research in this field should be aimed at assessing the potential benefit of GH therapy on BMD and PBM after children with GH have reached final height, identifying optimum dosage of GH to promote attainment of PBM after final height is reached, and finally to show whether a low PBM confers an increased risk of fracture in later life (Saggese *et al.* 1998).

References

Baroncelli GI, Bertelloni S, Ceccarelli C & Saggese G 1998 Measurement of volumetric bone mineral density accurately determines degree of lumbar undermineralization in children with growth hormone deficiency. *Journal of Clinical Endocrinology and Metabolism* **83** 3150–3154.

Bonjour JP, Ferrari S, Slosman D & Rizzoli R 1997 Apports calciques et croissance osseuse. *Archives de Pédiatrie* **4** 719–721.

Boot AM, Engels MAMJ, Boerma GJM, Krenning EP & De Muinck Keizer-Schrama SMPF 1997 Changes in bone mineral density, body composition, and lipid metabolism during growth hormone (GH) treatment in children with GH deficiency. *Journal of Clinical Endocrinology and Metabolism* **82** 2423–2428.

De Boer H, Blok GJ, Van Lingen A, Teule GJJ, Lips P & Van Der Veen EA 1994 Consequences of childhood-onset GH deficiency for adult bone mass. *Journal of Bone Mineral Research* **9** 1319–1326.

Kaufman J-M, Taelman P, Vermeulen A & Vanderweghe M 1992 Bone mineral status in growth hormone-deficient males with isolated and multiple pituitary deficiencies of childhood onset. *Journal of Clinical Endocrinology and Metabolism* **74** 118–123.

Matkovic V, Jelic T, Wardlaw GM, Ilich JZ, Goel PK, Wright JK *et al.* 1994 Timing of peak bone mass in caucasian females and its implications for the prevention of osteoporosis. *Journal of Clinical Investigation* **93** 799–808.

Rosen T, Wilhelmsen L, Landin-Wilhelmsen K, Lappas G & Bengtsson B-A 1997 Increased fracture frequency in adult patients with hypopituitarism and GH deficiency. *European Journal of Endocrinology* **137** 240–245.

Saggese G, Baroncelli GI, Federico G & Bertelloni S 1995 Effects of growth hormone on phosphocalcium homeostasis and bone metabolism. *Hormone Research* **44**(suppl) 55–63.

Saggese G, Baroncelli GI & Barsanti S 1996*a* Biochemical markers of bone turnover during growth hormone therapy. In *Paediatric Osteology – New Developments on Diagnostics and Therapy*, pp. 235–239. Ed E Schonau. Amsterdam: Elsevier.

Saggese G, Baroncelli GI, Bertelloni S & Barsanti S 1996*b* The effect of long-term growth hormone (GH) treatment on bone mineral density in children with GH deficiency. Role of GH in the attainment of peak bone mass. *Journal of Clinical Endocrinology and Metabolism* **81** 3077–3083.

Saggese G, Baroncelli GI, Bertelloni S, Cinquanta L & Di Nero G 1993 Effects of long-term treatment with growth hormone on bone and mineral metabolism in children with growth hormone deficiency. *Journal of Pediatrics* **122** 37–45.

Saggese G, Ranke MB, Saenger P, Rosenfeld RG, Tamaka T, Chaussaim JL *et al.* 1998 Diagnosis and treatment of growth hormone deficiency in children and adolescents: towards a consensus. *Hormone Research* **50**: 320–340.

Thientz G, Buchs B, Rizzoli R, Slosman D, Clavien H, Sizonenko PC *et al.* 1992 Longitudinal monitoring of bone mass accumulation in healthy adolescents: evidence for a marked reduction after 16 years of age at the level of the lumbar spine and femoral neck in female subjects. *Journal of Clinical Endocrinology and Metabolism* **75** 1060–1065.

Wuster C, Slenczka E & Ziegler R 1991 Increased prevalence of osteoporosis and arteriosclerosis in conventionally substituted anterior pituitary insufficiency: need for additional growth hormone substitution? *Klinische Wochenschrift* **69** 769–773.

Leptin

Overview of leptin pathways

L A Campfield and F J Smith

Center for Human Nutrition, University of Colorado Health Sciences Center, Denver, CO 8626, USA

Obesity is a major worldwide health problem that is increasingly prevalent in both adults and children. It is a complex, multifactorial disorder which is associated with such diseases as hypertension, Non-insulin dependent diabetes mellitus (NIDDM) and hypercholesterolaemia. Obesity is poorly managed and is a cause of significant and increasing morbidity in both the developed and developing world. Obesity is caused by a combination of genetic and environmental factors. Increased mass of adipose tissue is the result of an interaction between a genetic predisposition to metabolic efficiency responsible for 35–50% of the effect, and environmental and/or lifestyle factors. Obesity is also characterised by lowered insulin sensitivity in muscle and adipose tissue, insulin overproduction and hyperinsulinaemia, high rates of lipid (triglyceride) deposition in adipose tissue, and lipid abnormalities (Campfield *et al.* 1998). Because levels of leptin (from the Greek word for thin) *increase* in obesity, and some of its functions are unconnected with weight loss, we do not consider the term leptin wholly appropriate and prefer *OB protein*, as used throughout this chapter, until a more functionally precise name is found.

Experimental models of obesity

Before 1992, several animal models of obesity had been identified in the USA and Europe (Campfield *et al.* 1996, 1997*a*). The five mouse single-gene mutation models are listed here together with the protein affected by the mutation.

- *ob/ob* – OB protein
- *db/db* – OB receptor (OB-R)
- *fat/fat* – carboxypeptidase E
- *tub/tub* – TUB protein
- *agouti* – MC$_4$-R antagonist.

All these models are obese, obesity being very severe in *ob/ob* and *db/db*, less severe in *fat/fat*, *tub/tub*, and the (brilliant yellow) *agouti*. The agouti gene was cloned in 1992, though the etiology of obesity in this animal was not understood until 1997 (Huszar *et al.* 1997). Genetic deletion of the melanocortin 4 receptor (MC_4-R) revealed the involvement of a hitherto unknown pathway in the brain that could have a great impact on understanding of the neuroendocrine basis of obesity; this is discussed below (Campfield & Smith 1998).

In 1994, the *ob* gene was finally cloned by Friedman and colleagues at Rockefeller University USA, following a heroic effort; this event permanently changed the field of obesity (Zhang *et al.* 1994). The other genes listed above have also now been cloned. Carboxypeptidase E is an enzyme related to protein processing, although it is not known which proteins result in obesity. The TUB protein is found in the paraventricular nucleus of the brain, but its role in obesity is also unknown. Polygenic mouse models, and the *fa/fa* or Zucker rat, which has a defect in the OB-R, are also subjects of continuing investigation.

OB protein and its neuroendocrine functions

The OB protein signalling pathway

In mid-1995, the secreted OB protein predicted by Friedman and colleagues was shown to be biologically active by our research group and groups from Rockefeller University and the Amgen Corporation. Treating *ob/ob* mice with OB protein resulted in a complete reversal of the obese pathology (Campfield *et al.* 1996, 1997*a*).

Figure 1 schematically summarises the actions of OB protein on the brain, the autonomic nervous system and its consequent metabolic and behavioural changes.

Fat cells express *ob* mRNA and secrete OB protein at levels related to their volume. Up to 98% of the OB protein is bound to specific and non-specific binding proteins, and reaches the brain *via* a receptor-mediated translocation process in the brain microvessels (as occurs with insulin) (Golden *et al.* 1997). Once in the brain, OB protein generates a series of efferent pathways with effects on specific body functions (Campfield & Smith 1998).

The first effect of experimental exposure to OB protein to be recognised was suppression of food intake in lean and obese mice. Effects of OB protein on metabolism, hormonal regulation, reproductive function and energy expenditure have also been observed (Campfield *et al.* 1996, 1997*a*; Campfield & Smith 1998).

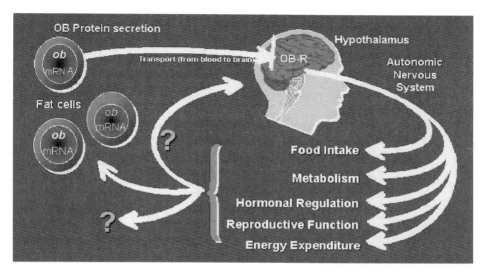

Figure 1 Schematic representation of the actions of OB protein *via* its receptor OB-R in the brain. Activation of the OB protein pathway triggers behavioural changes and activation of the autonomic nervous system leading to metabolic and behavioural changes affecting energy balance.

Food intake

Thus, OB protein is involved in a feedback system from the periphery to the brain which signals body fat mass, so that appropriate adjustments can be made in energy balance. In a non-obese individual, overeating increases fat mass, the volume of adipocytes and OB protein level, leading to a reduction in food-seeking behaviour and consequently also in body fat mass. However, the brain of an obese individual manifests a resistance to the action of OB protein analogous to insulin resistance in diabetes, the normal control system does not work, and fat mass increases (Campfield *et al.* 1996, 1997*a*; Campfield & Smith 1998).

Effects of OB protein

Injection of OB protein into the lateral ventricle of conscious mice results in a series of metabolic and behavioural responses (Campfield *et al.* 1996, 1997*a*). These responses to OB protein are specific (i.e. not due to a generalised suppression of food intake due to illness induced by the treatment). Reduction in *food intake* is dose- and time-dependent, and if maintained it leads to lowering of *body weight*. At the same time *body temperature* increases by about 0.5°C.

Metabolic responses to OB protein are equally impressive. Treatment results in an immediate decrease in serum *insulin* or *glucose* in hyperinsulinaemic or hyperglycaemic animals. Triglycerides and cholesterol also fall dramatically as lipids are transported into cells for oxidation, and the milky serum of the obese animal model becomes transparent. The *sympathetic nervous system* is also activated, metabolic rate and fat mobilisation increase, and the neuroendocrine *adaptation to starvation* is blocked (Ahima *et al*. 1996). In addition, OB protein helps maintain normal reproductive function. OB protein-deficient mice have low testosterone (males) and delayed ovulation (females) and are infertile. These alterations were reversed by treatment with OB protein; female mice became pregnant and successfully carried litters to term. (Campfield & Smith 1998).

Source and regulation of OB protein

White adipose tissue was the first source of OB protein to be identified and studied (Golden *et al*. 1997, Trayhurn *et al*. 1998). OB protein was later found to be produced also by brown adipose tissue, fat-containing differentiated bone marrow cells, muscles and other peripheral organs, and the placenta (Campfield & Smith 1998). Factors involved in the regulation of OB gene expression and the production of OB protein are listed in Table 1 (Trayhurn *et al*. 1998).

Table 1 Regulation of OB gene expression and OB protein production in humans

Gene expression
- induced by lipid accumulation
- increased by glucocorticoids
- increased by weight gain
- decreased by weight loss
- unaffected by acute diet, exercise, insulin, meals

OB protein production
- increased by lipid accumulation
- apparently affected by glucose metabolism
- increased by sustained positive energy balance
- decreased by sustained negative energy balance
- suppressed by fasting (18–24 hours)

As fat cell volume increases, OB mRNA and OB protein are increasingly produced. Short-term manipulations (e.g. meal regime, diet, exercise, insulin level) have immediate effects on OB gene expression and protein production in animals, but in humans such changes take several days to affect circulating OB protein levels. Longer-term changes (over more than 3 days) in energy intake or expenditure, or measurable changes in body weight do result in changed levels of the protein. Effects of administered OB protein on food intake can occur within minutes, on metabolism within hours, on changed gene expression in the brain within days, and effects on body fat, body composition, body weight and puberty, within days to weeks.

Effects of OB protein on the brain

The mechanism of action of OB protein on the brain has been investigated using intraperitoneal and intravenous administration, and direct injection into the lateral ventricle of the brain (intracerebroventricular; ICV). *In-situ* hybridisation studies revealed expression of OB-R where expected, in the lateral ventricles and choroid plexus. But the receptor was also expressed in several hypothalamic nuclei: in the arcuate nucleus, which secretes neuropeptide Y (NPY), the ventromedial hypothalamic (VMH) and the paraventricular nuclei, together with other brain areas known or thought to be involved in the regulation of energy balance and body weight (Mercer *et al.* 1996, Schwartz *et al.* 1996a).

Following ICV injection of OB protein, c-fos, gene expression was detected in these brain regions in immunoreactivity studies (van Dyck *et al.* 1996). Similar results were obtained using a transgenic mouse in which the promoter for the *c-fos* was spliced to *lac-Z*. Activation of *c-fos* promoter in these brain areas by ICV administration of OB protein led to production of a galactosidase that could then be visualised by staining. The fact that an important part of the response to OB protein is activation of the sympathetic nervous system has been confirmed by direct electrophysiological measurement of an increased rate of firing in sympathetic nerve bundles serving the kidney and brown fat of the rat (Haynes *et al.* 1997).

OB protein resistance

Many studies have confirmed the initial finding that serum levels of OB protein rise as body fat (% of total body weight) increases (Considine *et al.* 1996). This raises the question of why increasing levels of OB protein do not cause the behavioural and metabolic changes described above (particularly decreased food intake) leading to weight loss. Evidently individuals can show the phenomenon of OB protein resistance.

The spectrum of responsiveness to OB protein found in animal models extends from the completely unresponsive *db/db* mouse with inactive receptors to the highly sensitive *ob/ob* mouse. Between these extremes is the normal animal, which can be made obese by overfeeding with a high-fat diet – the diet-induced obesity (DIO) mouse. In DIO mice, the serum OB protein levels rise but they respond little or not at all to the protein. It seems that most obese humans also fit within this spectrum. We surmise that about one-third of obese people might respond well to treatment with OB protein, one-third partially and one-third not at all (Campfield & Smith 1998).

What is the physiological basis of OB protein resistance in obese people? Studies have focused on possible defects in the transport system by which OB protein enters the brain (Caro *et al.* 1996, Schwartz *et al.* 1996*b*). Other possibilities are peripheral receptor-mediated metabolic and/or endocrine effects, and the actions of neuronal networks in controlling centrally mediated actions of OB protein so that that the brain's own response to the protein becomes blunted.

Diminished central response to OB protein

We have investigated the last possibility, comparing changes in cumulative food intake after a single dose of OB protein in normal and DIO *akr/j* mice of various ages. Normal lean mice responded with a reduction of 50–70% in food intake over 6 hours, whilst DIO animals show a blunted response of around 30% (Campfield *et al.* 1997*b*).

So, lean animals show normal brain and peripheral responses to OB protein, and DIO animals show blunted responses both in the periphery and the brain. However, this blunting of sensitivity was reversible within weeks by returning them to the normal laboratory chow diet and subsequent weight loss. We hope that this weight-loss-induced increase in sensitivity to OB protein also applies to at least some obese people.

Peripheral effects of OB protein

Studies on the peripheral effects of OB protein have generated considerable controversy. Some workers argue that the crucial long-form OB protein receptor OB-R_L is found only within the brain, yet many peripheral effects have been reported (Table 2; Campfield 1999). The evidence for suppression of glucocorticoid secretion in the adrenal cortex by OB protein is particularly strong. In addition, very recent studies have shown that nerve ganglion cells within the pancreatic islets are rich in OB-R$_L$, suggesting how OB protein might be involved in the neural control of insulin secretion.

Table 2 Peripheral actions of OB protein (Campfield 1999)

Increased:
- insulin sensitivity
- glucose uptake

Decreased plasma levels of:
- cholesterol
- triglyceride
- glucose

Inhibition of:
- insulin secretion
- adrenocortical glucocorticoid secretion
- ovarian steroidogenesis

The role of OB protein in controlling energy balance

Dual pathways of OB protein action

OB protein appears to have two major classes of effect: acute modulation of synaptic transmission in the brain *via* ATP-sensitive potassium channels (also described in other chapters), and chronic regulation of gene expression: ICV administration of OB protein regulates the expression of the genes for NPY, pro-opiomelanocortin (POMC), corticotrophin-releasing hormone (CRH), agouti-related peptide (ARP) and anorexin (Campfield *et al.* 1998).

Effects of OB protein on obesity-related gene expression

OB protein can block the response to exogenous NPY, and modulate the gene expression of POMC, NPY and CRH. In addition, OB protein can control ARP and its blocking effects on the MC4-R, discussed below. Many neuronal networks are involved in the ultimate effects of these genes in the body; these networks are concerned with food intake, energy expenditure, metabolism and the autonomic nervous system. This network consists of clusters of receptors for the neuropeptides. Figure 2 schematically summarises the location of genes related to obesity in the mouse and human, and the neuronal networks believed to be involved (Campfield *et al.* 1998, Campfield & Smith 1998, Campfield 1999). OB protein, binding to its receptor, coordinates the production of a series of neuropeptides that act as receptors. The stylised representations of humans and mice in Fig. 2 indicate the locations of mutations that lead to obesity (e.g. lack of OB-R or MC$_4$-R).

So, OB protein seems to be the 'conductor of the orchestra', coordinating disparate neural pathways distributed throughout the various parts of the brain that are involved in energy balance to generate – in a lean animal – an appropriate response to energy intake, energy expenditure and the local environment. However, the response generated is inappropriate if the individual is obese.

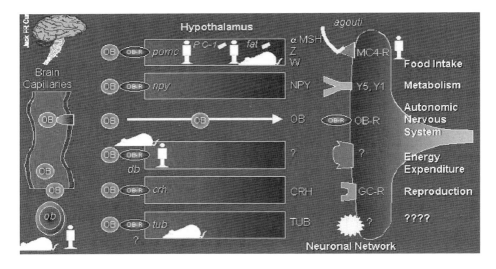

Figure 2 Schematic summary of the location of genes related to obesity in the mouse and human, and the neuronal networks believed to be involved in their activities. On the left, OB protein produced by fat cells acts *via* its transport system and brain receptor to coordinate the production of a series of neuropeptides that act as receptors. The middle shows an array of OB-responsive neurones (rectangles). OB binds to its receptor, OB-R and alters the expression of neuropeptide genes. Z, W, and ? denote unknown neuropeptides.The stylised representations of humans and mice show the locations of mutations that lead to obesity (e.g. lack of OB-R or TUB). OB, OB protein; OB-R, OB protein receptor; *pomc*, pro-opiomelanocortin gene; NPY, *npy*, neuropeptide-Y and its gene; CRH, *crh*, corticotrophin-releasing hormone and its gene; TUB, *tub*, TUB protein and its gene; ARP, *arp*, agouti-related peptide and its gene; MC4-R, melanocortin-4 receptor; GC-R, glucocorticoid receptor.

Melanocortin, OB protein, and energy balance

The melanocortin (MC) system is a promising area of potentially therapeutic developments in obesity. The five MC peptides interact with a family of G-protein coupling receptors (MC_1 to MC_5). The MC_3 and MC_4 receptors and their signalling pathways are involved in the regulation of food intake and energy balance in the following ways.

- Activating the receptor with peptide agonists (α-melanocyte stimulating hormone [α-MSH] analogues) inhibits food intake in rodents.
- Peptide antagonists stimulate food intake in rodents.
- The natural ligand for $MC_{3/4}$-R is believed to be a product of POMC processing, and probably not MSH.
- The MC_4-R knockout mouse shows obesity, increased food intake, hyperglycaemia, and extremely high levels of OB protein.
- The melanocortin signalling pathway appears to be downstream of the OB protein pathway and to interact at one or more points (Campfield 1999).

Conclusions and the future

- OB protein (leptin) is secreted by adipose tissue and provides a hormonal link between it and the brain. Its (long-form) receptor (OB-R_L) is localised in the hypothalamus and other brain areas involved in the regulation of energy balance.
- Increasing evidence shows OB protein to be crucial in regulating fat stores in rodents and primates (including humans) by coordinating the regulation of feeding behaviour, metabolism and energy balance *via* activation of the sympathetic nervous system.
- OB protein acts by regulating synaptic transmission, membrane channel dynamics, and gene expression so as to diminish fat mass to normal.
- Central sensitivity to OB protein is diminished in obesity, but can be restored by weight loss in mice.
- The identification of sites in the OB protein pathway at which brain sensitivity to OB protein is downregulated is an important goal of current research with major therapeutic implications.
- The melanocortin signalling pathway appears to be one of several parallel pathways which interact at various points with the OB protein pathway.
- Deleting the MC_4-R in the brain leads to decompensation of glucose regulation, elevation of OB protein, and expansion of adipose tissue mass. The vast therapeutic potential of an agonist for this G-protein-coupled receptor is being actively investigated worldwide.

References

Ahima RS, Prebakaren D, Mantzuros C, Ou D, Lowell B & Matzaros-Flier J 1996 Role of leptin in the neuroendocrine responses to fasting. *Nature* **382** 250-252.

Campfield LA 1999 Multiple facets of OB protein (leptin) physiology: Integration of central and peripheral mechanisms in the regulation of energy balance. In *Progress in Obesity Research 8*, pp. 327–335. Eds G Ailhaud & B Guy-Grand. London: Libbey.

Campfield LA & Smith FJ 1998 Overview: neurobiology of OB protein (leptin). *Proceedings of the Nutrition Society* **57** 429–440.

Campfield LA, Smith FJ & Burn P 1996 The OB protein (leptin) pathway – a link between adipose tissue mass and central neural networks. *Hormone and Metabolic Research* **28** 619–632.

Campfield LA, Smith FJ & Burn P 1997*a* OB protein: a hormonal controller of central neural networks mediating behavioral, metabolic and neuroendocrine responses. *Endocrinology and Metabolism* **4** 81–102.

Campfield LA, Smith FJ & Yu J *et al.* 1997*b* Dietary obesity induces decreased central sensitivity to exogenous OB protein (leptin) which is reversed by weight loss. *Society of Neuroscience Abstracts* **23** 815.

Campfield LA, Smith FJ & Burn P 1998 Strategies and potential molecular targets for obesity treatment. *Science* **280** 1383–1387.

Caro JF, Lolaczynski JW, Nyce MR *et al.* 1996 Decreased cerebrospinal-fluid/serum leptin ratio in obesity: a possible mechanism for leptin resistance. *Lancet* **348** 159–161.

Considine RV, Sinha MK, Heiman ML *et al.* 1996 Serum immunoreactive-leptin concentrations iin nomal-weight and obese humans. ral networks. *New England Journal of Medicine* **334** 292–295.

Golden PL, Maccagnan TJ & Pardridge WM 1997 Human blood–brain barrier leptin receptor. Binding and endocytosis in isolated human brain microvessels. *Journal of Clinical Investigation* **99** 14–18.

Haynes WG, Morgan DA, Walsh SA, Mark AL & Sivitz WI 1997 Receptor-mediated regional sympathetic nerve activation by leptin. *Journal of Clinical Investigation* **100** 270–278.

Huszar D, Lynch V, Fairchild-Huntress JH *et al.* 1997 Targeted disruption of the melanocortin-4 receptor: results in obesity in mice. *Cell* **88** 131–141.

Mercer JG, Hoggard N, Williams LM, Lawrence CB, Hannah LT & Trayhurn P 1966 Localization of leptin receptor mRNA and the long form splice variant (Ob-Rb) in mouse hypothalamus and adjacent brain regions by *in-situ* hybridization. *FEBS Letters* **387** 113–116.

Schwartz MW, Peskind E, Raskind M, Boyko EJ & Porte D, Jr 1996*a* Cerebrospinal fluid leptin levels: relationship to plasma levels and to adiposity in humans. *Nature Medicine* **2** 589–593.

Schwartz MW, Seeley RJ, Campfield LA, Burn P & Baskin DG 1996*b* Identification of targets of leptin action in rat hypothalamus. *Journal of Clinical Investigation* **98** 1101–1160.

Trayhurn P, Duncan JS, Hoggard N & Rayner DV 1998 Regulation of leptin production: a dominant role for the sympathetic nervous system? *Proceedings of the Nutrition Society* **57** 413–419.

Van Dijk G, Theile TE, Donahey JCK *et al.* 1996 Central infusions of leptin and GLP-1-(7-36) amide differentially stimulate c-FLI in the rat brain. *American Journal of Physiology* **271** R1096–R1100.

Zhang Y, Proenca R, Maffei M, Barone M, Leopold L & Friedman JM 1994 Positional cloning of the mouse obese gene and its human homologue. *Nature* **372** 425–431.

Genetic Insights in Paediatric Endocrinology and Metabolism
Eds S O'Rahilly and D B Dunger
BioScientifica Ltd, Bristol (1999)

Physiological studies of leptin

W Kiess, A Schmidt, P Englaro, J Kratzsch, J Deutscher, K Meyer and W Blum

Children's Hospital, University of Leipzig, D-04317 Leipzig, Germany

The populations of developed countries are becoming increasingly obese. For example, the proportions of men and women with a BMI (body mass index) of over 30 in England increased from 7% to 13% and from 12% to 16%, respectively, over the 7 years between 1986 and 1993 (Anon. 1993). The genetics of obesity is attracting more and more attention worldwide. However although Ob and Ob-R mutations are known to cause obesity and endocrine deficiencies in humans, Ob gene polymorphisms are uncommon in obese humans, and genetics may not represent the whole picture. This chapter focuses on leptin levels and effects in various conditions, human mutations, the relationships between obesity, BMI and puberty in children, eating disorders and obesity, neuroendocrine effects of leptin and, finally, leptin as a metabolic regulator during fetal and neonatal life.

The problem of obesity

A prospective questionnaire-based study conducted in our paediatric endocrinology unit showed that the activities of obese and age- and sex-matched non-obese children were significantly different. Compared to obese subjects, the lean children spent half as long in front of television or computer screens (2 vs 4 hours/day) and three times as long playing competitive sport (3 vs 1 hours/day); in addition, two-thirds took part in recreational sports, compared with only one-third of obese subjects (Table 1) (Dötsch *et al.* 1997).

Table 1 Activities of obese and non-obese children

Activity	Obese (*n* = 32)	Non-obese (*n* = 33)
Television/multimedia use (hours/day)	3.9 ± 1.3	1.9 ± 1.0*
Recreational sport (n/n)	11/32	21/33*
Competitive sport (hours/week)	1.1 ± 1.3	3.1 ± 3.2*

*$P < 0.01$

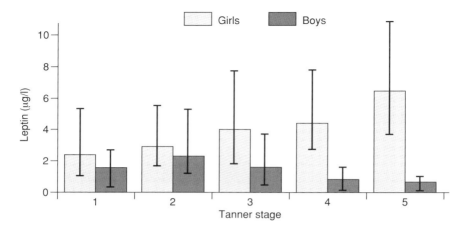

Figure 1 Leptin and pubertal development. Mean leptin levels increase steadily in girls during pubertal development, but in boys they peak early and then decline (after Blum *et al.* 1997*b*).

Leptin, fat mass, BMI and eating disorders

A strong relationship between serum leptin levels and BMI was shown in more than 700 normal healthy male and female Danish children (Blum *et al.* 1997). Females also had higher leptin levels than males.

In the Danish study, mean leptin levels rose as fat mass increased during pubertal development (Fig. 1). In girls, it increased steadily from around 2.5 µg/ml at Tanner stage 1 to over 6 µg/ml at stage 5; in boys, however mean levels peaked at about 2 µg/ml at stage 2 and fell to below 1 µg/ml at stage 5. Because of such changes, it is most important that any leptin levels measured during childhood and adolescence be related to normative data, taking into account sex, body fat mass and pubertal stage.

Patients (usually girls and young women) with severe anorexia nervosa may have a BMI as low as 12 (barely compatible with life) and their serum leptin levels are exceedingly low (< 0.2 µg/ml). Refeeding such patients causes their leptin levels to rise rapidly and overshoot. It is thought that these high leptin levels may actually lead to the refractoriness to treatment of these patients by making them stop eating (Köpp *et al.* 1997).

Leptin and endocrine function

Leptin is a key component of all the major neuroendocrine feedback loops, involving the somatotrophic, gonadal, adrenal and thyroid axes.

Corticosteroids

A small cohort of obese children (median 10 years), with BMIs of up to 45, had very high plasma leptin levels of 20–60 µg/l which were raised still further (to 25–80 µg/l) after a single dose of dexamethasone (Kiess *et al.* 1996). In addition studies in Cushing's disease have shown that chronic hypercortisolism is associated with hyperleptinaemia (Blum *et al.* 1997).

Type I diabetes

We have studied 13 prepubertal children with type I diabetes who attended our outpatient clinic. At the first manifestation of the disorder, and before exposure to exogenous insulin, their leptin levels (corrected for BMI, sex and pubertal stage) tended to be low (Kiess *et al.* 1998). In contrast, we found leptin levels to be high in more than 130 male and female patients with diabetes who were fairly well controlled by insulin treatment. The elevation of leptin reached significance ($P < 0.01$) in late puberty (Tanner stage 5) (Kiess *et al.* 1998).

Androgens

Testosterone is a potent suppressor of leptin production. Treating cultured differentiated human adipocytes with testosterone produces a clear dose-related suppression of leptin secretion *in vitro* (Fig. 2) (Wabitsch 1997). In addition, leptin levels in female to 'male' transexuals rapidly decline after

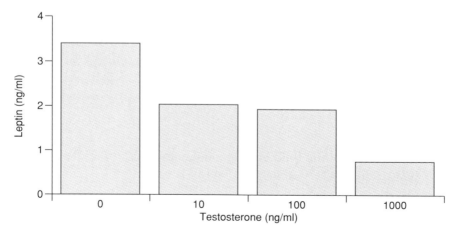

Figure 2 Testosterone suppresses leptin production by human adipocytes *in vitro* in a dose-related fashion (after Wabitsch *et al.* 1997).

testosterone treatment. Conversely, when males become 'female' and their testosterone levels are reduced, their leptin secretion increases (Elbers *et al.* 1997).

Growth hormone

Kriström and colleagues in Göteborg have recently shown that short-term (weeks or months) changes in serum leptin provide a strong metabolic marker for the growth response to growth hormone (GH) treatment in children (Kriström *et al.* 1998). We conducted a study on 40 children, some of whom showed a normal increase in GH levels in response to arginine infusions, while the others – who had GH deficiency (GHD) – did not respond. However, leptin levels did not change in either group over 3 hours. Although GH can lower leptin levels over the longer term, probably by reducing fat mass, it had no effect in the short term.

Maternal, fetal and neonatal leptin

Maternal serum and the placenta

It is important to remember that the placenta can synthesise not only leptin but also the different forms of Ob-R. Our own data show that, in general, maternal serum leptin increased during gestation and fell after birth. However, there was a wide variation in levels and patterns of change; some women showed high leptin levels throughout pregnancy, in others the level rose steeply from very low values, while others were intermediate. We have not yet identified any feature (e.g. fat mass, serum hormone levels) that would predict the various patterns of serum leptin, indicating that much remains to be learnt about the role of leptin in human gestation (Schubring *et al.* 1998).

Amniotic fluid

Leptin levels in amniotic fluid are high and comparable to maternal serum levels at the same stage of gestation (Table 2).

Cord blood and the neonate

Several research groups have shown that leptin levels in cord blood are closely correlated with birth weight (Schubring *et al.* 1997, Blum *et al.*

Table 2 Leptin levels in amniotic fluid and maternal serum at mid-gestation (*n* = 28)

	Leptin (ng/ml)		
	Mean ± sd	**Median**	**Range**
Maternal serum	13.9 ± 7.6	11.9	5.5–32.3
Amniotic fluid	11.6 ± 6.5	11.0	2.5–30.2

1997a). In 27 healthy newborns, leptin concentrations ranged from around 1 to 40 ng/ml, and levels in the umbilical artery or vein were very closely correlated (*r* = 0.98, *P* < 0.00001). The precise source of the leptin in cord blood is unknown. We have found that, within a few days of birth, serum leptin levels detected in heel-prick capillary blood from normal healthy babies decline steeply, and other workers have shown that they then rise to the higher levels characteristic of young children (Schubring *et al.* 1998).

Peripheral effects of leptin

Some very important questions remain about the peripheral effects of leptin. In addition to leptin mRNA in the placenta, we have found the expression of leptin and short- and long-form Ob-R in two tumours in children: a SK-N-MC neuroepithelioma cell line, and a lipoblastoma. We believe that leptin and Ob-R expression could be important for the development of other kinds of tumour (Deutscher *et al.* in press).

Conclusions and the future

- We strongly believe that leptin and Ob-R are constituents of the classic neuroendocrine networks in humans.
- However, it is still unclear what roles leptin might have in human disease, and whether those roles are restricted or ubiquitous.
- Leptin serum levels are high in obese subjects, during gestation and at birth, and normally decline after birth.
- Adolescents and young adults with type I diabetes have higher serum leptin levels than matched unaffected individuals.
- Leptin levels are normal in children with precocious puberty, but tend to be raised in Cushing's disease.
- Leptin levels might be useful as a marker for response to GH treatment in children with GHD.

- Many aspects of the possible peripheral actions of leptin remain to be investigated.
- Expression of leptin and Ob-R may be important for the development of some tumours.

References

Anon 1993 Epidemiology of obesity in the UK. *Lancet* **341** 621.

Blum WF, Kiess W & Rascher W (Eds) 1997*a* Leptin – the Voice of Adipose Tissue: *Proceedings of the European Leptin Symposium*. Mannheim: J&J Verlag Ambrosius Barth.

Blum WF, Englaro P, Hanitsch S *et al.* 1997*b* Plasma leptin levels in healthy children and adolescents: dependence on body mass index, body fat mass, gender, pubertal stage and testosterone. *Journal of Clinical Endocrinology and Metabolism* **82** 2904–2910.

Deutscher J, Meyer K, Blütters-Sawatzski R, Franke F & Kiess W in press Leptin and leptin receptor expression in a lipoblastoma in an 8-year-old girl. *Hormone Research*.

Dötsch J, Dittrich U, Rascher W & Kiess W 1997 Macht Fernsehen dick? – Beziehung zwischen Adipositas bei Kindern und Jugendlichen und Konsum alter und neuer Medien. *Der Kinderarzt* **28** 1351–1356.

Elbers JM, Asscheman H, Seidell JC, Frohlich M, Meinders AE & Gooren LJ 1997 Reversal of the sex difference in serum leptin levels upon cross-sex hormone administration in transsexuals. *Journal of Clinical Endocrinology and Metabolism* **82** 3267–3270.

Kiess W, Englaro P, Hanitsch S, Rascher W & Blum WF 1996 High leptin concentrations in serum of very obese children are further stimulated by dexamethasone. *Hormone and Metabolism Research* **28** 708–710.

Kiess W, Anil M, Englaro P, Rascher W & Blum WF 1998 Serum leptin concentrations in children and adolescents with insulin-dependent diabetes mellitus – relation to metabolic control, disease duration, weight and height. *European Journal of Endocrinology* **38** 501–509.

Köpp W, Blum WF, von Prittwitz S *et al.* 1997 Low leptin levels predict amenorrhea in underweight and eating disordered females. *Molecular Psychiatry* **2** 335–340.

Kristrom B, Carlsson B, Rosberg S, Carlsson LM & Albertsson-Wikland K for the Swedish Study Group for Growth Hormone Treatment 1997 Short-term changes in serum leptin levels provide a strong metabolic marker for the growth response to growth hormone treatment in children. *Journal of Clinical Endocrinology and Metabolism* **83** 2735–2741.

Schubring C, Kiess W, Englaro P, Rascher W & Blum WF 1997*a* Leptin concentrations in amniotic fluid, venous and arterial cord blood and maternal serum: high leptin synthesis in the fetus and inverse correlation with placental weight. *Journal of Clinical Endocrinology and Metabolism* **82** 1480–1483.

Schubring C, Siebler T, Englaro P *et al.* 1997*b* Rapid decline of leptin levels in healthy neonates after birth. *European Journal of Paediatrics* (letter) **157** 263–264.

Schubring C, Siebler T, Englaro P, Blum WF, Triep K & Kiess W 1998 Longitudinal analysis of maternal serum leptin levels during pregnancy, at birth and up to six weeks after birth: relation to BMI, skinfolds, sex steroids and umbilical cord blood leptin levels. *Hormone Research* **50** 276–283.

Wabitsch M, Blum WF, Muche R *et al*. 1997 Contribution of androgens to the gender difference in leptin production in obese children and adolescents. *Journal of Clinical Investigation* **100** 808–813.

Genetic Insights in Paediatric Endocrinology and Metabolism
Eds S O'Rahilly and D B Dunger
BioScientifica Ltd, Bristol (1999)

Lessons from leptin therapy

S Farooqi and S O'Rahilly[1]

University Departments of Medicine, Addenbrooke's Hospital, Cambridge
CB2 2QQ, UK

Obesity is an increasing problem in the western world in all demographic groups, children as well as adults. Much of the mortality associated with obesity is related to the comorbidities of adult coronary heart disease (CHD) and diabetes mellitus; in individuals with a body mass index (BMI: weight/height^2) of over 30 the relative risks of death from CHD are 2.4 for men and 2.3 for women; and the relative risks of developing diabetes are 8.3 and 10.6 for men and women respectively (Seidell 1997). But it should not be forgotten that obesity in childhood also leads to significant morbidity, associated in particular with poor mobility and sleep apnoea (Dietz & Robinson 1993).

The *ob/ob* mouse is severely obese – three times the weight of a normal mouse – hyperphagic, infertile and with corticosterone excess. This disorder is caused by mutations of the leptin gene (Zhang *et al.* 1994), and all the phenotypic abnormalities can be normalised by leptin treatment (Campfield *et al.* 1995, Halaas *et al.* 1995, Pelleymounter *et al.* 1996). In addition, in normal rodents, fasting results in a drop in serum leptin and a delay of several days in the onset of vaginal oestrus, which is almost totally abolished by the administration of leptin (Ahima *et al.* 1996).

The question remains, how relevant to humans are findings on leptin in mice? This paper discusses some new observations on congenital leptin deficiency in humans, compares this condition with leptin deficiency in *ob/ob* mice, and examines some of the lessons to be learnt from the treatment of human congenital leptin deficiency.

Congenital leptin deficiency in humans

We have identified two severely obese cousins within a highly consanguineous family of Pakistani origin, with congenital leptin deficiency due to a mutation in the leptin gene. Both were the offspring of first cousins and had normal-weight siblings. Numerous previous investigations had failed to account for their obesity. We found that both children were homozygous for a mutation in the leptin gene resulting in deletion of a single guanine base at codon 133 (Montague *et al.* 1997). This caused the insertion of 14 aberrant amino-acids and a premature stop codon, so that the resulting protein was truncated, lacking in particular a cysteine residue required for the formation of a disulphide bridge without which leptin would be predicted to lose its biological activity (Zhang *et al.* 1997). It appears that although this mutant protein is produced it cannot be secreted. Further detailed endocrine and metabolic data on the older child (child A) and her response to treatment with leptin are given next.

Clinical history of child A

Child A was of normal birthweight, but at 4 months of age began rapid weight gain that continued throughout childhood. Her weight when referred to us at age 9 was 94 kg (over 200 lb). At the age of 5 years she weighed about 54 kg and had already needed bilateral proximal tibial osteotomies to correct valgus deformities of the knees, and liposuction of lower limb fat to enable her to walk. The most striking feature of the history was extreme hyperphagia with evidence of impaired satiety, constant eating and waking at night to look for food. She had normal 24-hour urinary free cortisol and normal thyroid function with a normal response to thyrotrophin-releasing hormone (TRH) stimulation and was hyper-insulinaemic with a normal fasting blood glucose.

Analysis of body composition by dual energy X-ray absorptiometry (DXA) scanning revealed that child A had 59% body fat (normal range for a 9-year-old girl: 17–23%). Detailed measurements of energy expenditure were conducted; basal metabolic rate was performed using indirect calorimetry, and free-living energy expenditure measured by the doubly labelled water technique. These revealed that energy expenditure in child A was within the predicted range for her age after correcting for her high fat-free mass.

Subsequently, Stobel and colleagues have described a consanguineous Turkish family in whom three subjects were severely obese and leptin-deficient due to a missense mutation of the leptin gene. Two of these subjects were adults, a man and a woman, and had failed to undergo pubertal development. They had low concentrations of follicle-stimulating hormone (FSH) and luteinising hormone (LH) that responded to stimulation with gonadotropin releasing hormone (GnRH), consistent with hyogonadotropic hypogonadism, which can now be added to the phenotype of congenital leptin deficiency in humans (Strobel *et al.* 1998).

Treatment of congenital leptin deficiency with leptin

Just over 12 months before the time of writing, we began a clinical trial to ascertain whether human leptin could induce weight loss. It may be noted at the outset that our patient has remained well throughout the trial, and that no clinically significant adverse effects have been reported.

Study details

Recombinant human leptin (RmetHuleptin, AMGEN Inc) 0.028 mg/day has been given as a once-daily subcutaneous injection. The dose was calculated to achieve 10% of the normal leptin concentration on the basis of the patient's age, sex, and proportion of body fat, together with the known pharmacokinetics of leptin. The 10% level was chosen for safety reasons, and because *ob/ob* mice are known to be highly sensitive to small doses of leptin.

The primary outcome measure was a reduction in the rate of weight gain, and the patient was weighed at home daily at the same time. Further measurements carried out at 2-month intervals included: height and body composition (DXA scan, total body water); energy intake and expenditure; metabolic effects (insulin, glucose, lipid profile); endocrine effects gonadotropins, pelvic ultrasound); and leptin pharmacokinetics (serum leptin concentration and antibodies).

Effects of leptin treatment on body weight and energy balance

Within 12 days of the start of treatment, our patient began a significant loss of weight that continued over the 12-month period (Fig. 1). Over the first 12 months of treatment she lost 16.4 kg, at a consistent rate of 1.0–2.0 kg/month. DXA scans showed that 95% of the total weight lost was fat mass, which fell by 13.8 kg, from 55.4 kg to 41.6 kg. Sleeping metabolic rate decreased slightly after adjusting for the change in lean mass. A slight fall in free-living energy expenditure was probably attributable to her increased mobility.

Effects of leptin treatment on eating behaviour and metabolic parameters

Energy intake was assessed using an *ad libitum* test meal in which a large quantity of food (7 MJ) was provided. Prior to the start of treatment, the child immediately consumed almost all the food available, and continued to report feelings of hunger. With 7–10 days of the start of leptin treatment, a marked change in the patient's eating behaviour was seen; she stopped

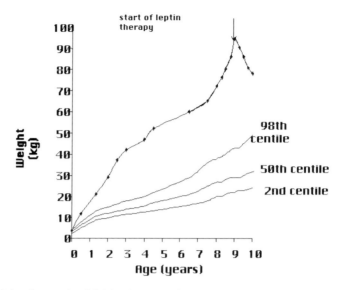

Figure 1 Weight change in child A prior to and after the start of leptin therapy.

demanding food, became content with small amounts of food at a time, ate slowly, could be distracted from eating, and became more selective, rejecting some foods. Energy intake at the first test meal following the start of treatment decreased by 41% to 3.91 MJ, which was sustained throughout the 12-month period of leptin treatment.

There was no significant change in plasma glucose, insulin, total, low density lipoprotein (LDL) and high density lipoprotein (HDL) cholesterol, triglycerides, together with a fall in serum non-esterified fatty acids consistent with her degree of weight loss.

Leptin 24-hour pharmacokinetics

Peak serum leptin concentrations of 5.5 ng/ml occurred 4 hours after administration. After 6 weeks of treatment, non-neutralising leptin antibodies began to develop, but no effect of these was apparent on either clinically significant side-effects or on weight loss. However, the antibodies did appear to influence pharmacokinetics. Serum leptin levels prior to injection and 4 hours after injection were increased in the presence of antibodies. In addition, the peak serum leptin concentration occurred much later (at 8 h rather than at 4 h), which would be compatible with a delay in renal clearance. This effect is seen in obese subjects (who are leptin-sufficient) and in *ob/ob* mice treated with this preparation of recombinant human leptin (M McCamish, personal communication).

Endocrinology, growth and puberty

We found no evidence of disturbance to the thyroid, adrenal or somatotrophic axes during treatment. The patient's IGF-1 levels have been normal before and during treatment, and her growth rate did not change. Interestingly, she had always been tall, her height continuing to lie on the 91st centile, even though her parents' height predicted a height on the 25th centile. The baseline radiograph at chronological age 9 showed that her bone age was already markedly advanced (12.5 years) but, after 12 months of treatment with leptin, bone age had increased by only 1 year, in line with chronological age.

In view of the known loss of fertility in *ob/ob* mice, we were particularly interested in the effects of leptin treatment on child A's reproductive axis. She was clinically prepubertal at baseline despite her advanced bone age. Serum levels of oestradiol and androgens, and the ultrasound appearance of the uterus and ovaries remained prepubertal during leptin treatment. However, both basal and luteinising hormone releasing hormone (LHRH)-stimulated gonadotropin levels increased. Stimulated 1-hour levels of FSH rose from 3.5 U/l at baseline to 8.9 U/l at 12 months, and LH levels from 1.0 to 2.9 U/l.

These findings were followed up with pulsatility studies, involving blood sampling at 10-minute intervals for 6 hours during the day and 12 hours overnight. During the day, serum levels of both LH and FSH were low and with minimal pulsatility, but at night there were frequent pulses of both FSH and LH which would be consistent with early puberty.

Congenital leptin deficiency in humans and mice

From our own findings with child A, and the extensive literature on the *ob/ob* mouse, the similarities and differences between the phenotypes of congenital leptin deficiency in humans and mice can be summarised (Table 1; Bray & York 1971).

Affected mice and humans are of normal birthweight, and have severe hyperphagia and obesity of early onset. However energy expenditure is normal in human leptin deficiency, in comparison to *ob/ob* mice, which are hypometabolic – indeed hypothermic. The absence in humans of the elevated glucocorticoid concentrations seen in *ob/ob* mice may explain the

Table 1 Comparisons of congenital leptin deficiency in humans and obese mice

	Leptin-deficient humans	*ob/ob* mice
Birthweight	normal	normal
Fat mass	↑↑↑	↑↑↑
Appetite	↑↑↑	↑↑↑
Energy expenditure	normal	↓↓↓
Serum glucose level	normal	↑↑
Serum insulin level	↑↑	↑↑↑
Adrenal function	normal	↑↑↑
Thyroid function	normal	?
Gonadal function	↓↓↓	↓↓↓
Linear growth	normal	↓

differences in plasma insulin and linear growth, which are strain-dependent in mice.

Conclusions and the future

- Leptin plays a key role in the regulation of body weight in humans.
- Congenital leptin deficiency is a novel syndrome of human obesity, and we have shown for the first time that treatment with leptin can induce significant and consistent weight loss in a severely obese child with this condition.
- The continuation of this patient's treatment and the treatment of her affected cousin, which began in late 1998, are providing rare opportunities to study the regulatory role of leptin in human energy balance and neuroendocrine function.

References

Ahima RS, Prabakaran D, Mantzoros C, Qu D, Lowell B, Maratos-Flier E *et al.* 1996 Role of leptin in the neuroendocrine responce of fasting. *Nature* **382** 250–252.

Bray GA & York DA 1971 Genetically transmitted obesity in rodents. *Physiological Reviews* **51** 598–646.

Campfield LA, Smith FJ, Guisez Y, Devos R & Burn P 1995 Recombinant mouse OB protein: evidence for a peripheral signal linking adiposity and central neural networks. *Science* **269** 546–549.

Dietz WH & Robinson TN 1993 Assessment and treatment of childhood obesity. *Pediatric in Review* **14** 337–343.

Halaas JL, Gajiwala KS, Maffei M, Cohen SL, Chait BT & Rabinowitz D 1995 Weight-reducing effects of the plasma protein encoded by the obese gene. *Science* **269** 543–546.

Montague CT, Farooqi IS, Whitehead JP, Soos MA, Rau H & Wareham NJ 1997 Congenital leptin deficiency is associated with severe early-onset obesity in humans. *Nature* **387** 903–908.

Pelleymounter MA, Cullen MJ, Baker MB, Hecht R, Winters D, Boone T *et al.* 1996 Effects of the obese gene product on body weight regulation in ob/ob mice. *Science* **269** 540–543.

Seidell JC 1997 Time trends in obesity: an epidemiological perspective. *Hormone and Metabolic Research* **29** 155–158.

Strobel A, Issad T, Camoin L, Ozata M & Strosberg AD 1998 A leptin missense mutation associated with hypogonadism and morbid obesity. 1998 *Nature Genetics* **18** 213–215.

Zhang Y, Proenca R, Maffei M, Barone M, Leopold L & Friedman JM 1994 Positional cloning of the mouse obese gene and its human homologue. *Nature* **372** 425–432.

Zhang F, Basinski MB, Beals JM, Briggs SL, Churgay LM & Clawson DK 1997 Crystal structure of the obese protein leptin-E100. *Nature* **387** 206–209.

Summary

Genetic Insights in Paediatric Endocrinology and Metabolism
Eds S O'Rahilly and D B Dunger
BioScientifica Ltd, Bristol (1999)

Summary of the conference

I Hughes

Department of Paediatrics, Addenbrooke's Hospital, Hills Road, Cambridge CB2 2QQ, UK

This was an excellent meeting in which the metabolic and endocrine aspects of many disorders were brought together. The guest lectures were presented by a galaxy of international experts in the field. **Professor Krishna Chatterjee** reviewed the whole range of nuclear transcription factors in relation to his work on thyroid disease, and revived interest in congenital hypothyroidism, an extremely important condition for paediatric endocrinologists. The cause of thyroid agenesis is a crucial question to be answered. **Dr Allen Spiegel** encompassed almost the whole of endocrinology in his discussion of the G-protein-related peptides. It is hoped that he will take up the suggestion to replace such terms as pseudopseudo-hypoparathyroidism with names describing the pathophysiology. **Professor Marcus Pembrey** gave a thoughtful philosophical lesson on endocrine genetics that introduced many novel concepts: the conflict hypothesis, the positioning of genes between mono- and biallelic expression, transgenerational effects, homologue chromosome kissing, allele crosstalk, and even Patagonian giants. Returning to classical endocrinology, **Professor Guiseppe Sagesse** presented data on growth hormone (GH) and its effect on bone. He gave useful practical advice to paediatricians. GH-deficient children should continue to receive GH for a few more years after they stop growing in height, in order to achieve peak bone mass and so prevent fractures in adult life. One would add that the enormous variation in height of the general population must be influenced in some way by multiple gene polymorphisms. The presentation of **Professor Raj Thakker** on multiple endocrine neoplasia (MEN) represented a lesson in how to tackle and find a gene using a wide variety of techniques. In a short time he summarised an enormous amount of work over many years in tracking down the MENIN gene.

Turning to the main symposia, the combined presentation of **Professor Aynsley-Green** and **Dr Mark Dunne** brought the audience up to date with hyperinsulinism and with the devastating condition of persistent hyperinsulinism of infancy, emphasising in the process a recurring theme – the value of studying rare disorders. Not only are they interesting in their own right, but the pathophysiology of a rare disorder often provides vital information about related common disorders and about normal physiology. These speakers also emphasised the essential role of collaboration in modern-day research. The Human Genome Project will soon bring to an end the era of human gene sequencing. We are beginning to enter a new era of molecular physiology, taking molecules – as these speakers described – 'from the bench to the bedside'. In addition, the patch-clamp experiments described in their talk gave insights into the design of new drugs to help patients with hyperinsulinism, and even hinted at a cure for diabetes.

Dr Charles Stanley gave a beautiful account of glutamate dehydrogenase deficiency, showing also that the condition, well known as leucine-sensitive hypoglycaemia, is now explained by a gene mutation. **Dr Edward Novotny** described a variety of new nuclear magnetic resonance spectroscopy techniques that can visualise hypoglycaemia in the brain directly and non-invasively.

Moving into the field of diabetes, **Professor Stephen O'Rahilly** (Chairman and Co-organiser of the conference) took the audience at speed through the area of insulin resistance, drawing on the results of *in vitro* work performed by himself and his team to focus on such topics as chimaeric receptors and the use of tailored antibodies to correct gene defects. **Professor Alan Moses** tackled the challenging task of providing insights into the treatment of insulin resistance (the insulin pathways are not easy to understand). Possible therapeutic manoeuvres include the use of insulin-like growth factor (IGF-I) and troglitazone. Concern was expressed about many side effects of IGF-I – particularly at high doses. **Dr Andrew Hattersley** described maturity-onset diabetes of the young (MODY), a relatively straightforward condition that is well-defined in terms of genetic abnormalities. The condition illustrates the fact that not everything in one's phenotype at birth is due to maternal nutrition and environment. The diabetes symposium was rounded off by **Professor John Todd** who gave an excellent summary of the genetics of type 1 diabetes. No single gene will provide the whole answer for this T-cell-mediated inflammatory disorder. Diabetes is only one example of a disease state in which polymorphisms of the genome have phenotypic expression. He also emphasised that successful therapy of type 1 diabetes will involve a polypharmaceutical, not a single-drug approach.

In the area of overgrowth syndromes, **Dr Jill Clayton-Smith** gave an excellent overview of such rare dysmorphic disorders as Simpson–Golabi–Behmel, Sanfillipo, Sotos and Proteus syndromes. **Dr Eamonn Maher** focussed on Beckwith–Wiedemann syndrome (BWS), a complex disorder involving multiple gene defects and one or more imprinted centres.

The discovery of mutations in the p57^{KIP2} gene is now throwing light on BWS, which opens a huge area of continuing research. **Dr Katherine Woods** described the only known case of IGF-I deletion in humans. She later described the relationship between genotype and gene polymorphisms in the determination of birth weight. Low birth weight may involve a 'thrifty genotype', and not be solely a function of maternal influence.

The story of leptin continues. As **Professor O'Rahilly** has said, 'Fat is not just a lump of boring lard; it is an endocrine organ' that is exercising the minds of many physiologists, biochemists and molecular geneticists. **Dr Arthur Campfield** pointed out that obesity is a major problem in the Western world and exhorted paediatric endocrinologists to 'bring obesity back' into their clinics. In the light of the leptin story, a more sympathetic approach to obese children referred to clinics may help find the answers to this major problem. Leptin and the leptin receptor are expressed in many body tissues, and even – which Dr Campfield did not mention – in the very early human blastocyst, at the four-cell stage. **Dr Michel Aubert**, who has been working in the puberty area for many years, emphasised that neuropeptide Y and leptin are two major factors among the many involved in puberty. The nature of the trigger for normal puberty is still not understood. However, again the study of rare disorders is helping to elucidate an aspect of normal physiology: the importance of leptin in reproductive function. **Dr Wieland Kiess** provided useful data on leptin levels. Although they are directly correlated with BMI and total body fat, leptin levels show huge variation – presumably a function of the diffuse nature of the endocrine organ. Dr Kiess stressed the importance of viewing such measures in relation to normative data on age, gender and pubertal stages. The clinical study involving successful treatment of a congenitally leptin-deficient obese child reported by **Dr Sadaf Farooqui** again emphasises the value to be gained from studying even one or two patients with a rare disorder.

In all, the Cambridge meeting provided a feast of endocrinology consumed in the delightful ambience of St John's College. Due credit must be paid to the Scientific Committee for their programme planning and to Serono Laboratories who supported and organised the conference. The Cambridge Serono Symposia are now a well-established component of the international endocrine meeting diary.

Author index

Subject index

Page numbers in *italics* indicate figures appearing away from their text.